Schofield & Sims

Mental Arithmetic
Book 5 Answers

Teacher's Notes

Introduction

Mental arithmetic skills are fundamental to achievement in mathematics. The purpose of *Schofield & Sims Mental Arithmetic* is to provide differentiated practice tests in key areas of the maths curriculum, to be administered regularly. In addition, there is a clear focus on how number is communicated using both number vocabulary and non-verbal mathematical signs and processes.

The series consists of seven pupil books – all of them conforming to a standard layout. This ensures that pupils are not presented with too many variables at once. The *Mental Arithmetic 5* pupil book contains:
- 36 tests grouped into three sections – Sections 1, 2, and 3 – each containing 12 tests
- two Progress Tests, with Results Charts for recording individual pupils' Progress Test results
- four Check-up Tests, together covering number, approximations, money, measures, fractions, ratios, percentages, angles, shapes, perimeter, area and volume.

Parts A, B and C

Each of the 36 tests that form the bulk of the book appears on a single page and is divided into three parts (A, B and C) – the specific content of the parts is as described on the back cover. The division into parts enables you to ensure that differentiation takes place: Parts A and B use pictures, symbols and simple language wherever possible so that pupils with reading difficulties will not be disadvantaged. It is suggested that one test is taken each week and that Parts A, B and C are set on separate days. Since speed with accuracy is important, a time limit of 10 minutes per part is recommended. However, you may adjust this as appropriate.

Answering the test questions

The material in each section is graded so that, before any test question is attempted, the work will usually have been covered in class. The coverage of each Section is outlined on the Contents page.

The term 'mental arithmetic' implies that *answers only* are required. For this reason, the books are presented in a one-per-pupil format, so that answers can be written in the blanks. If the pupils are allowed rough paper for workings out, remember that their responses will be slower.

> **Please note:** You should explain to the pupils that the device ▪ , used in Part A, indicates a missing number.

Marking

A separate book of answers, like this one, is available to accompany each pupil book. When the pupils have completed a test you may read out the answers as they mark their own work. If work has been done in small groups or individually, the pupils could refer to the answer book themselves.

Progress Tests

The Progress Tests, each consisting of 20 items, appear at the end of Sections 1 and 2. These are designed as timed tests, to take exactly 10 minutes each. Each Progress Test should be administered on four different occasions, under test conditions that are as similar as possible each time. So that the test can be reused, ask pupils to write their answers on a separate sheet of paper, rather than in the pupil book. Alternatively, you may photocopy a Progress Test page that has not been completed, and have the pupils write their answers on the copy. After each attempt at a Progress Test has been marked, record each pupil's results on the Results Chart provided, or invite pupils to do so themselves.

> **Please note:** Photocopying restrictions have been waived on the two Progress Tests and the two Results Charts that appear in the pupil book (pages 16, 17, 30 and 31). **Photocopying other pages – from the pupil book or from this book of answers – is not allowed.**

Check-up Tests

The Check-up Tests at the back of the book focus on specific topics. Administer them at the end of the school year or when a pupil finishes the book: the results will give you an insight into any areas of weakness. When the pupil moves up to a new class, the completed book should be given to the new teacher so that he or she can plan work accordingly.

Contents

Section 1   Test 1

A

		ANSWER
1	60 000 + 3000 + 70 + 8	63 078
2	$5 \times 8 \times 7$	280
3	$8\,\ell\,550\,m\ell - \frac{1}{4}\ell = \boxed{\ }\ \ell$	$8.3\,\ell$
4	$\frac{5}{6}$ of £42	£ 35
5	(a) $3\frac{5}{8} = \frac{\boxed{\ }}{8}$	(a) $\frac{29}{8}$
	(b) $6\frac{4}{5} = \frac{\boxed{\ }}{5}$	(b) $\frac{34}{5}$
6	£7·30 + $\boxed{\ }$ TENS = £10	27 TENS
7	3650 m = $\boxed{\ }$ km $\boxed{\ }$ m	3 km 650 m
8	$180° - (86° + 64°)$	30°
9	(a) $\frac{19}{50} = \boxed{\ }$ %	(a) 38%
	(b) 0.64 = $\boxed{\ }$ %	(b) 64%
10	5.08 = $\boxed{\ }$ thousandths	5080 thousandths
11	$6^3 - 6^2$	180
12	£4·50 ÷ 7 = $\boxed{\ }$ p rem. $\boxed{\ }$ p	64p rem. 2p

B

		ANSWER
1	Write in words the number which is 400 less than 50 000.	forty-nine thousand six hundred
2	Find in £s the total of 18p, 16p, 25p and 9p.	£ 0·68
3	Change these improper fractions to mixed numbers. (a) $\frac{35}{6}$	
	(b) $\frac{63}{8}$	(a) $5\frac{5}{6}$ (b) $7\frac{7}{8}$
4	Find the difference between 3 FIFTIES and the sum of 12 FIVES and 6 TWOS.	78p
5	How many times is 25 g contained in 4 kg?	160
6	Find the change from a £5 note after spending £2·03.	£ 2·97
7	$\boxed{2 \quad 3 \quad 5 \quad 7 \quad 9}$	
	Which of these numbers are factors of 56?	2 and 7
8	What percentage of 2 litres is 400 mℓ?	20%
9	Approximate	
	(a) 29.56 to the nearest whole one	(a) 30
	(b) 180 370 to the nearest 1000.	(b) 180 000
10	What fraction in its lowest terms is equal to (a) 95%	
	(b) 0.04?	(a) $\frac{19}{20}$ (b) $\frac{1}{25}$
11	Find the cost of 700 g at 90p per kg.	63p
12	Find the area of a square of 20-cm side.	400 cm²

C

		ANSWER
1	How many thousandths must be added to 9.037 to make 10?	$\frac{963}{1000}$
2	Find the change from £1·50 after buying 2 kg potatoes at 36p per $\frac{1}{2}$ kg.	6p
3	A boy faces SE and turns clockwise through $1\frac{1}{2}$ right angles. In which direction is he now facing?	W
4	A car travels 40 km in 30 min. How many km will it travel at this speed in $\frac{3}{4}$ h?	60 km
5	A metal bolt weighs 250 g. How many bolts weigh 50 kg?	200

6 EMPLOYEES IN A FACTORY

From the diagram find what fraction of all the employees are
(a) men   (b) women?   (a) $\frac{3}{5}$ (b) $\frac{1}{4}$

(c) If the total number of employees is 400 how many are under 18?   (c) 60

		ANSWER
7	Amy spends 30% of her money on a book and saves 60%. If she had 20p left how much had she at first?	£ 2·00

8

The triangle ABC is inscribed in a semicircle. If ∠ ABC is 42°, find
(a) ∠ BAC   (a) 90°
(b) ∠ ACB.   (b) 48°

		ANSWER
9	A bus departs at 19.47 and arrives at its destination 1 h 16 min later. Write the time of its arrival.	21.03
10	The area of a rectangular path is 75 m². It is 50 cm wide. How long is it in m?	150 m
11	A map is drawn to a scale of 1 mm to 100 m. Find the distance in km represented by a line 2.6 cm long.	2.6 km

12

The measurements of the box are given. Find the area of
(a) the sides   (a) 85 cm²
(b) the ends   (b) 60 cm²
(c) the top and bottom.   (c) 102 cm²

Section 1 Test 2

A

			ANSWER
1	Write $10 \times 100 \times 100$ (a) in figures	(a)	100 000
	(b) in words.	(b)	one hundred thousand
2	£7·60 × 20		£ 152
3	$1 = \frac{1}{4} + \frac{3}{8} + $		$\frac{3}{8}$
4	10 − 6.32		3.68
5	320 min = h min		5 h 20 min
6	$\frac{4}{5}$ of £4·50		£ 3·60
7	$0.175\,\ell = $ mℓ		175 mℓ
8	25% of £7·00		£ 1·75
9	2.4 m + 55 cm = cm		295 cm
10	(a) 1% of £1 = p	(a)	1p
	(b) 13% of £1 = p	(b)	13p
11	4050 mm = m		4.05 m
12	$\frac{3kg\ 420\ g}{6} = $ g		570 g

B

			ANSWER
1	Multiply the sum of 3.6 and 2.4 by 0.4.		2.4
2	Name the date which is 5 months before 1st February.		1st September
3	47° 92° 138° 89° 210°		
	Which of these angles are		
	(a) acute angles	(a)	47°, 89°
	(b) obtuse angles?	(b)	92°, 138°
4	Three packets have a mass of 450 g, 800 g and 230 g. Find their total mass in kg.		1.480 kg
5	By how many mm is 780 mm greater than 0.5 m?		280 mm
6	How many TWENTIES have the same value as £9·00?		45
7	Write in km/h a speed of 18 km in 10 min.		108 km/h
8	How many times is 0.625 less than 625?		1000
9	Write as a percentage (a) 17p of £1·00	(a)	17%
	(b) 300 g of 1 kg.	(b)	30%
10	300 mℓ cost 27p. Find the cost per ℓ.		90p
11	Approximate (a) $10\frac{3}{10}$ to the nearest whole one	(a)	10
	(b) £13·52 to the nearest £.	(b)	£ 14
12	Find the area of a rectangle measuring 7 m long and 1.3 m wide.		9.1 m²

C

			ANSWER
1	By how many pennies is 13 TENS less than the total of 2 FIFTIES and 9 FIVES?		15p
2	Of 300 children in a school 43% were boys. (a) What percentage were girls?	(a)	57%
	(b) How many boys were there in the school?	(b)	129
3	28° x 37° Find the angle marked x.		115°
4	A can holds 5 ℓ when full. Find the quantity of water in ℓ and mℓ when the can is $\frac{3}{4}$ full.		3 ℓ 750 mℓ
5	$\frac{3}{5}$ $\frac{3}{4}$ $\frac{7}{10}$ $\frac{13}{20}$		
	Which of these fractions is (a) the largest (b) the smallest?	(a) $\frac{3}{4}$ (b)	$\frac{3}{5}$
6	The attendance at a football match was 6843. (a) Approximate this number to the nearest thousand.	(a)	7000
	(b) Find the difference between the actual and the approximate numbers.	(b)	157
7	Sophie's home is 850 m from school. How far in km does she walk in a week of 5 days, making one return journey each day?		8.5 km
8	A card 60 cm by 40 cm is cut into strips each 8 cm wide. (a) How many strips are cut?	(a)	5
	(b) Find the total length of the strips in m.	(b)	3 m
9	A box containing 60 envelopes costs £3·68. Find the cost of 15 envelopes.		92p
10	Find the age in years and months of both children on 1st September 2015.		

DATES OF BIRTH

Josh	1.02.'99
James	1.10.'96

	Josh	16 years	7 months
	James	18 years	11 months

11	The price of milk is increased by 8%. If £4 each week was paid to the milkman, how much more is there now to pay?		32p
12	60° A B (a) What fraction of the circumference of the circle is the arc AB?	(a)	$\frac{1}{6}$
	(b) If the circumference measures 56.4 cm, find the length of the arc AB.	(b)	9.4 cm

5

A

		ANSWER
1	Write as a decimal $100 + \frac{3}{10} + \frac{7}{1000}$.	100.307
2	$4\frac{3}{4} \times 8$	38
3	£2 − (35p + 63p)	£ 1·02
4	$1\frac{1}{4}\ell$ − 900 mℓ = mℓ	350 mℓ
5	3.8 − 2.76	1.04
6	35% = $\frac{\quad}{100}$ = $\frac{\quad}{20}$	$\frac{35}{100} = \frac{7}{20}$
7	g × 100 = 4 kg	40 g
8	7.43 a.m. to noon = h min	4 h 17 min
9	$\frac{553\ mm}{7}$ = cm mm	7 cm 9 mm
10	830 g × 5 = kg	4.150 kg
11	(a) 10% of £12·00	(a) £ 1·20
	(b) 70% of £12·00	(b) £ 8·40
12	$\frac{2}{3}$ of £1·08 = £	£ 0·72

B

		ANSWER
1	Multiply the sum of 29 and 18 by 8.	376
2	Decrease £3·50 by 20%.	£ 2·80
3	Find the reflex angle AOB.	313°
4	How many times is 0.7 m contained in 28 m?	40
5	How many days in 26 weeks?	182
6	What percentage of 1 kg is 550 g?	55%
7	Find the time in h and min from 09.40 to 13.25.	3 h 45 min
8	What is the cost of 2.5 kg at 18p per $\frac{1}{2}$ kg?	90p
9	What percentage of the circle is	
	(a) shaded	(a) 30%
	(b) coloured	(b) 10%
	(c) plain?	(c) 60%
10	Approximate	
	(a) 27.9 km to the nearest km	(a) 28 km
	(b) 3.450 kg to the nearest kg.	(b) 3 kg
11	20 articles cost £8·20. Find the cost of 5.	£ 2·05
12	The area of a rectangle is 30 m². Its width is 2.5 m. Find its length.	12 m

C

		ANSWER
1	An article which cost 43p was paid for with a £1 coin. Which three coins were given as change?	50p 5p 2p
2	In the number 30.632, how many times is the 3 marked y less than the 3 marked x ?	1000
3	When a number is divided by 8 the answer is $6\frac{3}{8}$. What is the number?	51
4	Four children receive these amounts of pocket money: 55p, 66p, 45p and 50p. Find the average.	54p
5	A cask contained 75 ℓ of cider. 10% of it was wasted. Find in ℓ and mℓ the quantity which remained.	67 ℓ 500 mℓ
6	ABC is an isosceles triangle. Find the angles at the base.	
	∠ ABC	78°
	∠ ACB	78°
7	{ 1, 2, 3, 6, 9, 18, 36 } Two members of this set of factors of 36 are missing. Which are they?	4 and 12
8	Sita's mass increased from 40 kg to 42 kg. What was the increase	
	(a) as a fraction	(a) $\frac{1}{20}$
	(b) as a percentage?	(b) 5%
9	Which is the better buy, A or B, and by how much? (A) Eight 250-g packs of rice at 45p per pack or (B) 2 kg of rice at £1·60 per kg.	B by 40p
10	From the rectangular card the shaded part is cut off. Find its area.	20 cm²
11	A tin of floor stain costing £4·50 will cover 5 m²	
	(a) How many tins must be bought to cover a floor 5 m by 3 m?	(a) 3
	(b) What is the cost?	(b) £ 13·50
12	The cube has sides each measuring 5 cm. Find	
	(a) its surface area	(a) 150 cm²
	(b) how many cm cubes can be fitted into the cube.	(b) 125

Section 1 Test 4

A

		ANSWER
1	$(7 \times 10^3) + 6$	7006
2	$\frac{3}{4} + \frac{1}{8} + 2$	$2\frac{7}{8}$
3	$100 - (8 \times 9)$	28
4	$0.085\, \ell = \quad m\ell$	$85\, m\ell$
5	5.07×6	30.42
6	£27 ÷ 100 = ▢ p	27p
7	650 g + 0.5 kg = ▢ kg	1.150 kg
8	$\frac{1}{20} = \frac{5}{100} = \quad \%$	$\frac{5}{100} = 5\%$
9	2 h 37 min + 1 h 33 min = ▢ h ▢ min	4 h 10 min
10	75% of 30 kg = ▢ kg ▢ g	22 kg 500 g
11	$8\,\overline{)\,32.48}$	4.06
12	(a) 18p = ▢ % of £1	(a) 18%
	(b) 45 cm = ▢ % of 1 m	(b) 45%

B

		ANSWER
1	Write as a decimal 3085 thousandths.	3.085
2	From the total of 83p and £1·06 take 70p.	£ 1·19
3	Find the product of 0.6 and 0.9.	0.54
4	Find the total number of days in the months of September, October and November.	91
5	When a number is divided by 9 the answer is 64 rem. 5. What is the number?	581
6	3 articles cost 87p. Find the cost of 2 articles.	58p
7	What fraction in its lowest terms is (a) 800 g of 1 kg (b) 150 mℓ of $\frac{1}{2}\ell$?	(a) $\frac{4}{5}$ (b) $\frac{3}{10}$
8	How many times greater is 5030 than 5.03?	1000
9	(a) 20% of £8·50	(a) £ 1·70
	(b) 60% of £8·50	(b) £ 5·10
10	Approximate (a) £1·095 to the nearest penny	(a) £ 1·10
	(b) 9.150 ℓ to the nearest $\frac{1}{2}\ell$.	(b) 9 ℓ
11	0.5 kg of grapes costs £1·50. Find the cost of 700 g.	£ 2·10
12	Find the area of the triangle.	72 cm²

9 cm / 16 cm

C

		ANSWER
1	The volume of a tank is 1950 cm³. How many ℓ of water does it hold? (1 cm³ = 1 mℓ)	1.950 ℓ
2	A car travels 360 km on 40 ℓ of petrol. How many km per ℓ is this?	9
3	$243 \times 15 = 3645$ Find (a) 2.43×15	(a) 36.45
	(b) 24.3×1.5.	(b) 36.45
4	The bill for meals in a restaurant was £20·40. 10% was added as a service charge. How much was added?	£ 2·04
5	Buses run at intervals of 18 min. Find the times of the next two buses after 09.37.	09.55 10.13
6	In the triangle ABC, find ∠ ACB	50°
	∠ BAC.	75°
7	The mass of a TEN coin is 6.5 g. What is the mass in kg of £20 in TENS?	1.3 kg
8	A line 9 cm long represents the distance flown by an aeroplane. If the line is drawn to a scale of 1 mm to 50 km, find the actual distance.	4500 km
9	The price of articles in a shop was reduced by 5p in the £1. Find (a) the reduced price of an article costing £30	(a) £ 28·50
	(b) the reduction as a percentage.	(b) 5%
10	A rectangle measures 3 m long and 70 cm wide. Find its area in m².	2.1 m²
11	7 articles cost £2·80. (a) What fraction of £2·80 will 3 articles cost?	(a) $\frac{3}{7}$
	(b) Find the cost of 5 articles.	(b) £ 2·00
12	A block of wood is 1.5 m long with a section 3 cm square. How many 3-cm cubes can be made from the block?	50

3 cm / 3 cm

Section 1　Test 5

A

			ANSWER
1	Write in figures		
	(a) 0.7 million	(a)	700 000
	(b) 1.2 million.	(b)	1 200 000
2	19p + 27p + 63p		£ 1·09
3	12.65 km = ▪ m		12 650 m
4	$2\frac{7}{8} + 1\frac{1}{8} + 1\frac{1}{4}$		$5\frac{1}{4}$
5	(a) 1% of twenty thousand	(a)	200
	(b) 100% of four hundred and nine	(b)	409
6	$\frac{x}{6} = 8.53$　Find the value of x.		51.18
7	1.65 m − 95 cm = ▪ cm		70 cm
8	$\frac{3}{25} = \frac{▪}{100} = ▪\%$		$\frac{12}{100} = 12\%$
9	350 mℓ × 9 = ▪ ℓ		3.150 ℓ
10	4.050 kg + ▪ g = 5 kg		950 g
11	35p × 100		£ 35·00
12	970 ÷ 40 = ▪ rem. ▪		24 rem. 10

B

		ANSWER
1	How many thousandths are there in five point nought eight?	5080 thousandths
2	Find the average of 2.7, 3.6 and 1.8.	2.7
3	How many times is 250 mℓ contained in 3.5 ℓ?	14
4	Increase £240 by 5%.	£ 252
5	How many h and min from midnight to 1.45 p.m.?	13 h 45 min
6	27　42　54　63　72	
	Which of these numbers is a multiple of 4, 6 and 9?	72
7	What is the mass in kg of 6 packets each having a mass of 230 g?	1.380 kg
8	25% of a sum of money is 73p. What is the whole amount?	£ 2·92
9	Find the cost of 50 g at £2·60 per $\frac{1}{2}$ kg.	26p
10	$\frac{705}{8}$　Write the answer to the nearest whole one.	88
11	$\frac{3}{8}$ of a sum of money is 24p. Find $\frac{7}{8}$ of the sum of money.	56p
12	The perimeter of a square is 1.2 m. Find	
	(a) the length of a side in cm	(a) 30 cm
	(b) the area of the square in cm².	(b) 900 cm²

C

			ANSWER
1	Jamil received 12p change from £2 after buying 4 tins of beans. Find the cost per tin.		47p
2	Ellie is facing SW. In which direction is she facing if she turns		
	(a) 45° clockwise	(a)	W
	(b) 180° anticlockwise?	(b)	NE
3	The average mass of three bags of sand is 25 kg. If two of the bags have masses of 20 kg and 28 kg respectively, find the mass of the other bag.		27 kg
4	$\frac{1}{4}$　$\frac{3}{10}$　15%　$\frac{3}{20}$　$\frac{18}{100}$　3%		
	Which of these fractions or percentages are equal to 0.15?		$\frac{3}{20}$　15%
5	Find the smallest sum of money which must be added to £2·45 to make it exactly divisible by 9.		7p
6	The chart shows the percentages of adults and children who live on an estate of 720 people.		

MEN	WOMEN	BOYS	GIRLS
13%	12%	35%	?

			ANSWER
	(a) What percentage are girls?	(a)	40%
	(b) Find the total number of men and women.	(b)	180
7	A 12-day cruise started on Friday, 26th March. On which day and date did the cruise end?		Tuesday, 6th April
8	A barrel when $\frac{5}{8}$ full holds 60 litres. How many ℓ does it hold when		
	(a) $\frac{1}{8}$ full	(a)	12 ℓ
	(b) $\frac{3}{4}$ full?	(b)	72 ℓ
9	The price of a ticket is increased from £1 to £1·18. What is the percentage increase?		18%
10	The circumference of the circle measures 31.4 cm. Its radius is 5 cm. Find the perimeter of the semicircle.		25.7 cm
11	The dimensions of a triangle are base 15 cm, height 12 cm. Find the area of a triangle of the same base but one third of the height.		30 cm²
12	(a) How many cm cubes fit exactly into the bottom of the box?	(a)	45
	(b) How many such layers are required to fill the box?	(b)	6

6 cm　5 cm　9 cm

Section 1 Test 6

A

		ANSWER
1	$(5 \times 10^3) + (3 \times 10) + 7$	5037
2	$2.805\,\ell = \square$ ml	2805 ml
3	£0·07 × 50 = £ $\square$	£ 3·50
4	44 mm + 28 mm + 32 mm = $\square$ cm	10.4 cm
5	$\frac{7}{8}$ of 640	560
6	$1\frac{3}{4}$ kg − $\square$ g = 1.2 kg	550 g
7	(0.25 × 4) ÷ 100	0.01
8	5% of 3000	150
9	(a) $\frac{6}{25} = \frac{\square}{100} = \square$ % (a) $\frac{24}{100} =$ 24%	
	(b) $\frac{9}{20} = \frac{\square}{100} = \square$ % (b) $\frac{45}{100} =$ 45%	
10	0.46 + $\square$ = 0.505	0.045
11	3 m 40 cm × 7 = $\square$ m	23.8 m
12	£34 ÷ 8	£ 4·25

B

		ANSWER
1	How many fifties are there in one hundred thousand?	2000
2	1 tonne = 1000 kg. Write in tonnes (a) 2050 kg (a)	2.050 tonnes
	(b) 800 kg. (b)	0.8 tonne
3	Write 59 sixths as (a) an improper fraction (a)	$\frac{59}{6}$
	(b) a mixed number. (b)	$9\frac{5}{6}$
4	Find the missing numbers in the series. 3.65, 3.8, 3.95, $\square$, $\square$	4.1 , 4.25
5	Find in degrees the difference between the temperatures 7°C and −8°C.	15°
6	100 pencils cost £7·00. Find the cost of (a) 1 pencil (a)	7p
	(b) 30 pencils. (b)	£ 2·10

7

PARALLELOGRAM

Find
∠ ADC   53°
∠ BCD.   127°

		ANSWER
8	What percentage is (a) £7 of £20 (b) 28 kg of 40 kg? (a) 35% (b) 70%	
9	How many days inclusive are there from 27th May to 9th June?	14
10	30% of a sum of money is 27p. Find 100% of the money.	90p
11	Divide £2·00 by 7. Give the answer to the nearest penny.	29p

12

3.5 cm

Find
(a) the diameter (a)   7 cm
(b) the circumference of the circle. (b) 21.98 cm

(C = πd; π = 3.14)

C

		ANSWER
1	The population of a city increased from $\frac{3}{4}$ million to 1.1 million. Write in figures the number by which the population increased.	350 000
2	A packet of salt contains 400 g. (a) How many packets can be made from 3.5 kg? (a)	8
	(b) How many g are left? (b)	300 g
3	During a week a motorist drove 503.6 km. Find to the nearest km his average daily journey.	72 km
4	Which of these numbers do not change in value if the noughts are omitted? 0.740 3.016 0570 0.364	0.740 , 0.364

5

PENTAGON

The perimeter of a regular pentagon is 36 cm. Find in mm
(a) the length of one side (a)   72 mm
(b) the length of one side of a regular octagon of the same perimeter. (b)   45 mm

		ANSWER
6	In a test a boy scored 87% of a possible mark of 200. How many marks did he lose?	26
7	Nadeen's date of birth is 20.4.'98. She is 1 year 9 months younger than Emma. What is Emma's date of birth?	20.7.'96

8

ABC is a right-angled triangle. Find the exterior angles marked x and y.

∠ x = 142°   ∠ y = 128°

		ANSWER
9	1 ℓ of water has a mass of 1 kg. If a jar contains 5650 ml of water, find the mass of the water to the nearest $\frac{1}{2}$ kg.	5.5 kg
10	William's wage was increased from £120 to £132 per week. Find the increase (a) as a fraction in its lowest terms (a)	$\frac{1}{10}$
	(b) as a percentage of the original wage. (b)	10%
11	The mass of an empty box is 870 g which is $\frac{3}{10}$ of its total mass when filled with fruit. Find its total mass in kg.	2.9 kg
12	Carpet is 50 cm wide. Find the length required to cover a surface the area of which is 8.5 m².	17 m

A

		ANSWER
1	Write in figures 1.25 million.	1 250 000
2	£1·06 + 7p + 94p	£ 2·07
3	1.35 kg − 900 g = g	450 g
4	$4.139 = 4 + \frac{}{100} + \frac{}{1000}$	$\frac{13}{100} + \frac{9}{1000}$
5	$2\frac{3}{8} \times 5$	$11\frac{7}{8}$
6	10 000 ÷ 8	1250
7	2 h 15 min − 50 min = h min	1 h 25 min
8	$\frac{7}{10}$ of £1·60	£ 1·12
9	$0.85 = \% = \frac{}{20}$	$85\% = \frac{17}{20}$
10	46 cm × 30 = m	13.80 m
11	(a) 3% of £1 = p	(a) 3p
	(b) 12% of £1 = p	(b) 12p
12	$\frac{2\,\ell\,250\,m\ell}{5} = m\ell$	450 mℓ

B

		ANSWER
1	Multiply the difference between 1.8 and 2.5 by 6.	4.2
2	What is the average in mℓ of $\frac{1}{2}\ell$, $\frac{1}{4}\ell$ and 150 mℓ?	300 mℓ
3	How many times can a length of 25 cm be cut from 4.5 m?	18
4	What percentage of (a) 30 is 15	(a) 50%
	(b) £1 is 23p?	(b) 23%
5	Find the two missing numbers in this series. $4\frac{1}{2}$, $4\frac{1}{8}$, $3\frac{3}{4}$, ,	$3\frac{3}{8}$, 3
6	$\frac{1}{2}\ell$ of vinegar costs £1·20. Find the cost of 200 mℓ.	48p
7	Write the 24-hour clock time which is 27 min later than 23.36.	00.03
8	The total mass of 9 equal packets is 6 kg 750 g. Find in g the mass of 1 packet.	750 g
9	5% of a sum of money is £0·65. What is the whole amount?	£ 13
10	By how many tenths is $6\frac{1}{5}$ greater than $5\frac{1}{2}$?	$\frac{7}{10}$
11	If 1 m is divided into 7 equal parts, what is the length of each part to the nearest cm?	14 cm
12	The area of a rectangle is 205 cm². Its width is 10 cm. Find its length.	20.5

C

		ANSWER
1	How many thousandths must be added to 4.206 to make 5? Write the answer as a decimal.	0.794
2	Katie saves 8p per week for a year. How much are her total savings?	£ 4·16
3	A rail journey takes 2 h 35 min. If a train arrives at 21.05, what was the time of its departure?	18.30
4	There are 50 sheets of paper in a packet. How many packets can be made from twenty thousand sheets?	400
5	ABCD is a square of 9-cm side. Find (a) the area of the square	(a) 81 cm²
	(b) the area of the shape which is shaded.	(b) 81 cm²
6	The cash price of a radio is £60. By how much is its price increased if it is paid for by 8 equal instalments each of £9?	£ 12
7	A car travels 105 km in 2 h 30 min. Find its average speed in km/h.	42 km/h
8	The diagram shows how the weekly housekeeping money is spent. What percentage is spent on (a) food	(a) 60%
	(b) heat and light?	(b) 30%
	(c) If the total money is £125 per week, how much is saved?	(c) £ 12·50
9	3 bananas have a mass of 400 g. How many bananas will give a mass of 2.4 kg?	18
10	Josh spent $\frac{1}{4}$ of his money on sweets and $\frac{1}{2}$ of the remainder on bus fares. What fraction of his money was left?	$\frac{3}{8}$
11	The gross mass of a can of water is 6.350 kg. In the can there are $5\frac{1}{2}\ell$ of water. What is the mass of the can in g?	850 g
12	Find (a) the area of the bottom of the box	(a) 34 cm²
	(b) the volume of the box.	(b) 170 cm³
	In each case give the unit of measurement.	

10

Section 1   Test 8

A

		ANSWER
1	$3^4 = 3 \times 3 \times 3 \times 3 =$	81
2	6.09×7	42.63
3	3 TENS + 7 FIVES = £0·73 – ▨ p	8p
4	20% of 3 kg 600 g	720 g
5	$\frac{3}{10} + \frac{7}{10} + \frac{9}{10}$	$1\frac{9}{10}$
6	$\frac{9072}{9}$	1008
7	1.750 ℓ – ▨ mℓ = 800 mℓ	950 mℓ
8	$x + x + x + x = 108$ Find the value of x.	27
9	£2·08 = ▨ TWOS	104 TWOS
10	285 min = ▨ h ▨ min	4 h 45 min
11	(a) $\frac{4}{5} =$ ▨ %	(a) 80%
	(b) $\frac{3}{10} =$ ▨ %	(b) 30%
12	$(3 \times 56p) + (2 \times 56p)$	£ 2·80

B

		ANSWER
1	Write as a decimal the sum of 7 tenths and 39 hundredths.	1.09
2	Decrease £4·50 by 8p in the £1.	£ 4·14
3	By how many g is 2.345 kg less than $2\frac{1}{2}$ kg?	155 g
4	Calculate the reflex angle AOC.	219°

		ANSWER
5	What is the annual interest on £650 at 7%?	£ 45·50
6	A car travels 27.4 km in 20 min. Find its speed in km/h.	82.2 km/h
7	Write in figures the date (a) 6 months later than 1st Oct.'03	(a) 1.4.'04
	(b) 4 months before 1st Mar.'96.	(b) 1.11.'95
8	750 mℓ of cooking oil cost 72p. Find the price per ℓ.	96p
9	A board measures 5 m long and 20 cm wide. Find its area in m².	1 m²
10	$8\overline{)£\ \ \centerdot\ \ \ }$ $\begin{array}{c}1\centerdot 0\ 9\end{array}$ What is the missing amount of money?	£ 8·72
11	Approximate (a) 199 503 to the nearest 1000	(a) 200 000
	(b) 7 kg 350 g to the nearest $\frac{1}{2}$ kg.	(b) 7.5 kg
12	The base of the triangle is double the height. Find the area of the triangle.	81 cm²

C

		ANSWER
1	A medicine bottle holds 150 mℓ. Find in ℓ the contents of 20 bottles.	3 ℓ
2	300 people attended a concert. 63% were adults and the remainder children. (a) What percentage were children?	(a) 37%
	(b) How many adults were present?	(b) 189
3	The average height of three children is 130 cm. The heights of two of the children are 105 cm and 140 cm respectively. Find the height of the third child.	145 cm
4	Find the change from £2 and a FIFTY after spending 93p, £1·17 and 28p.	12p
5	$1.8 \times 0.7 = 1.26$ Now write the answers to (a) 0.18×0.7	(a) 0.126
	(b) 1.8×70.	(b) 126
6	The area of the circle from which the quadrant is cut is approximately 58.1 cm². Find (a) the diameter of the circle	(a) 8.6 cm
	(b) the area of the quadrant to the nearest cm².	(b) 15 cm²

		ANSWER
7	The price of 250 g of butter was increased from 60p to 66p. Find this increase as a percentage of the original price.	10%
8	A plan is drawn to the scale of 1 mm to 50 m. What distance in km is represented by a line 10 cm long?	5 km
9	Eight parcels of equal mass together have a mass of 7 kg 400 g. Find (a) the mass in g of 4 parcels	(a) 3700 g
	(b) what fraction of the total mass is the mass of 3 parcels.	(b) $\frac{3}{8}$
10	How many tiles each 10 cm square are required to cover the kitchen floor?	1500

		ANSWER
11	5 articles cost £3·78. Find the cost of one article to the nearest penny.	76p
12	A skeleton model of a 6-cm cube is made by fastening together lengths of straws. Find the total length required.	72 cm

Section 1 Test 9

A

		ANSWER
1	Write in figures five hundred and two thousand one hundred and four.	502 104
2	$7.3 = 10 \times$ ▓	0.73
3	£5 − (£3·66 + 54p)	80p
4	$\frac{1}{3}$ of 2.850 ℓ = ▓ mℓ	950 mℓ
5	9.6 cm − 58 mm = ▓ mm	38 mm
6	1% of 23.5 kg = ▓ g	235 g
7	1000 − (8 × 9)	928
8	350 g + 725 g + 875 g = ▓ kg	1.950 kg
9	$1\frac{1}{4} + \frac{7}{8} - \frac{1}{2}$	$1\frac{5}{8}$
10	(a) 5% of £36·00	(a) £ 1·80
	(b) $2\frac{1}{2}$ % of £36·00	(b) 90p
11	$10 \times y = 0.35$ Find the value of y.	0.035
12	$\frac{£21·56}{7}$	£ 3·08

B

		ANSWER
1	Write 35 out of 50 as (a) a fraction in its lowest terms	(a) $\frac{7}{10}$
	(b) a percentage.	(b) 70%
2	By how many degrees does the temperature rise from −3°C to 9°C?	12°C
3	How many kg are there in (a) $\frac{1}{8}$ tonne	(a) 125 kg
	(b) 0.8 tonne?	(b) 800 kg
4	Find the change from a £10 note after paying for 3 articles at £2·90 each.	£ 1·30
5	By how many min is $2\frac{3}{4}$ h longer than 1 h 55 min?	50 min
6	8.25 ℓ of juice is needed to fill 10 bottles. How many mℓ of juice in each bottle?	825 mℓ
7	$\frac{1}{2} = 0.5$; $\frac{1}{4} = 0.25$ Write $\frac{1}{8}$ as a decimal fraction.	0.125
8	0.3 of a sum of money is £1·50. Find the whole amount.	£ 5
9	What decimal fraction when multiplied by 9 gives 6.3 as the answer?	0.7
10	2 3 4 5 6 7 8 9 Which of these numbers are factors of 64?	2 , 4 , 8
11	Material costs £7·86 per m. Find to the nearest penny the cost of 20 cm.	£ 1·57
12	RHOMBUS The perimeter of this rhombus is 15.6 cm. Find the length of one side in mm.	39 mm

C

		ANSWER
1	A joint of meat had a mass of 2 kg 700 g. 10% of its mass was lost in cooking. Find the loss in g.	270 g
2	A shop opens from 8.30 a.m. to noon and 1.30 p.m. to 6 p.m. (a) How many h is the shop open?	(a) 8 h
	(b) What fraction of a day is it open?	(b) $\frac{1}{3}$
3	AC and BD are the diagonals of the rectangle and ∠ BDC is 30°. Find the angles marked x, y and z.	∠ x 60° ∠ y 120° ∠ z 60°
4	25% of a sum of money is £9·76. What is $12\frac{1}{2}$ % of this amount?	£ 4·88
5	Place a decimal point in each of these numbers so that the value of the figure 9 is 9 thousandths. (a) 309	(a) 0.309
	(b) 79	(b) 0.079
	(c) 2009	(c) 2.009
6	Water from a full $\frac{1}{2}$-ℓ measure is poured into a jar. When the jar was filled there were 115 mℓ left. What was the capacity of the jar in cm³ ?	385 cm³
7	A tin of beans costs 34p. How much is saved per tin by buying a pack of 6 for £1·92?	2p
8	$\frac{1}{4}$ million people watched football matches during a week. The number was increased by 1% the next week. What was the increased number?	252 500
9	A metal bar is 20 cm long with a square cross-section of 4-cm side. Find its volume.	320 cm²
10	The approximate distance by road from London to Glasgow is 623 km. How long to the nearest $\frac{1}{2}$ h will it take a motorist to make the journey if his average speed is 80 km/h?	8 h
11	By how much is 5% of £25 greater than 4% of the same amount?	25p
12	A garden consists of a lawn 9 m by 6.5 m surrounded by a path 50 cm wide. Find (a) the length	(a) 10 m
	(b) the breadth	(b) 7.5 m
	(c) the area of the garden.	(c) 75 m²

Section 1 Test 10

A

		ANSWER
1	$2.703 = \frac{\square}{10} + \frac{\square}{1000}$	$\frac{27}{10} + \frac{3}{1000}$
2	$\frac{4}{5}$ of 1.5 kg = $\square$ g	1200 g
3	£0·76 × 30	£ 22·80
4	50 000 − 970	49 030
5	2 h 37 min + 7 h 53 min = $\square$ h	$10\frac{1}{2}$ h
6	2 ℓ 700 mℓ × 8 = $\square$ ℓ $\square$ mℓ	21 ℓ 600 mℓ
7	$10^4 = 10 × 10 × 10 × 10 = \square$	10 000
8	2 FIFTIES + 3 TWENTIES + 10 FIVES = £ $\square$	£ 2·10
9	(a) 27p = $\square$ % of £1·00	(a) 27%
	(b) 35 cm = $\square$ % of 1 m	(b) 35%
10	$4\frac{3}{8} × 7$	$30\frac{5}{8}$
11	(a) 50% of £3·96	(a) £ 1·98
	(b) 75% of £9·00	(b) £ 6·75
12	Write as decimal fractions (a) $\frac{2}{5}$	(a) 0.4
	(b) $\frac{3}{8}$	(b) 0.375
	(c) 79%.	(c) 0.79

B

		ANSWER
1	By how many is 1.4 million greater than nine hundred thousand?	500 000
2	Subtract 37p from the total of 29p, 21p and 4p.	17p
3	What mass in kg is 6 times 4 kg 300 g?	25.8 kg
4	By how many times is 8.3 greater than 0.083?	100
5	What fraction in its lowest terms is equal to (a) 16%	
	(b) 45% ? (a) $\frac{4}{25}$ (b) $\frac{9}{20}$	
6	10 articles cost £2·90. Find the cost of (a) 1 article	(a) 29p
	(b) 3 articles.	(b) 87p
7	A line is 49 mm longer than the line AB. A ———————— B 7 cm 5 mm What is the length of the line in mm?	124 mm
8	How many times is 2.5 contained in 100?	40
9	How many days inclusive from 19th Feb. 2006 to 5th March 2006?	16
10	$\frac{108.9}{6}$ Write the answer to the nearest whole one.	18
11	Find the cost of 1.3 kg at 20p per 100 g.	£ 2·60
12	The perimeter of a rectangle is 85 cm. Its length is 28 cm. Find its width.	14.5 cm

C

		ANSWER
1	If £1·00 can be exchanged for 1·38 Euros, how many Euros are received for £50?	69 €
2	When a number is divided by 7 the answer is $208\frac{5}{7}$. Find the number.	1461
3	A can holds 5.6 ℓ of water. What is the volume of the can in cm³ ?	5600 cm³
4	$\frac{3}{8}$ $\frac{1}{5}$ $\frac{7}{10}$ $\frac{5}{12}$ $\frac{1}{6}$ $\frac{3}{5}$ $\frac{1}{3}$ $\frac{8}{12}$ Which of these fractions are (a) greater than $\frac{1}{2}$ (b) less than $\frac{1}{4}$?	(a) $\frac{7}{10}, \frac{3}{5}, \frac{8}{12}$ (b) $\frac{1}{5}, \frac{1}{6}$
5	Four 5-mℓ spoonfuls of medicine are taken daily. How many days will a bottle holding 0.3 ℓ last?	15
6	A lawn fertiliser is applied at the rate of 50 g to 1 m². How many bags each containing 1 kg are required to treat a lawn 8 m long and 5 m wide?	2
7	On 21st December the sun rises at 08.03 and sets at 15.50. How many h and min of daylight are there on this day?	7 h 47 min
8	Megan saved a TEN every week for a year. Her father then gave her a gift of 20% of her savings. How much did father give her?	£ 1·04
9	A piece of wood 1 m 36 cm long is cut into two pieces so that one piece is three times as long as the other. Find the length of each piece.	34 cm 102 cm
10		A	B	C	Base	8 cm	9 cm	10 cm	Height	6 cm	4 cm	4.8 cm Which of the triangles A, B and C have the same area?	A , C
11	The price of a shirt costing £17 was increased by 7p in the £. Find (a) its increased price	(a) £ 18·19
	(b) the increase as a percentage.	(b) 7%
12	(a) What fraction of the area of the circle is the shaded sector?	$\frac{1}{8}$
	(b) If the circumference of the circle measures 471 mm, find to the nearest mm the length of the arc AB.	59 mm

13

Section 1   Test 11

A

			ANSWER
1	(a) $2^5 = 2 \times 2 \times 2 \times 2 \times 2 = $ ▢	(a)	32
	(b) $10^5 = $ ▢	(b)	100 000
2	5 FIVES + 7 TENS − 9 TWOS = ▢ p		77p
3	(73 + 9) = 150 − ▢		68
4	10.085 km = ▢ m		10 085 m
5	$\frac{y}{100} = 10.64$ Find the value of y.		1064
6	6.358 = 63 tenths + ▢ thousandths		58 thousandths
7	550 g × 6 = ▢ kg		3.3 kg
8	£36·5 ÷ 10 = £ ▢		£ 3·65
9	75° + 65° + 90° + ▢ ° = 360°		130°
10	$\frac{3}{10}$ of 0.3 m = ▢ cm		9 cm
11	8% of £3·00		24p
12	17.2 ÷ 20		0.86

B

			ANSWER
1	Write these improper fractions as mixed numbers. (a) $\frac{74}{5}$	(a)	$14\frac{4}{5}$
	(b) $\frac{39}{7}$	(b)	$5\frac{4}{7}$
2	Find in ℓ the total of 830 mℓ, 360 mℓ and 170 mℓ.		1.360 ℓ
3	3.03 3.33 3.3 3.333		
	Of these numbers which is (a) the greatest	(a)	3.333
	(b) the smallest?	(b)	3.03
4	Increase £370 by 10%.		£ 407
5	Write as a fraction in its lowest terms (a) 15 mm of 15 cm		
	(b) 25 min of 1 h.	(a) $\frac{1}{10}$ (b)	$\frac{5}{12}$
6	Find the difference between 0.394 and 0.4.		0.006
7	Which of these numbers are multiples of both 5 and 8? 16, 25, 40, 64, 90, 120		40 , 120
8	$\frac{3}{8}$ of a sum of money is 45p. Find $\frac{1}{2}$ of the sum of money.		60p
9	Find to the nearest cm one seventh of $6\frac{1}{4}$ m.		89 cm
10	What sum of money is 200% of £170?		£ 340
11	Find the cost of 2.5 kg at 74p per 500 g.		£ 3·70
12	The perimeter of this parallelogram is 72 cm. Find the length of the sides AD and BC.		11 cm

PARALLELOGRAM
A — B
D — C
25 cm

C

			ANSWER
1	By how many is $(10^3 + 16)$ greater than $(10^2 + 16)$?		900
2	George's date of birth is 27th Nov. '04. How old will he be in years and months on 1st Sept. 2020	15 years	9 months
3	Sophie received a gift of £16. She saved 90% of the money and spent the rest. (a) What percentage did she spend?	(a)	10%
	(b) How much did she save?	(b) £	14·40
4	Each of the equal angles in this isosceles triangle is twice the size of the third angle. Find the size of (a) the third angle	(a)	36°
	(b) the equal angles at the base.	(b)	72°
5	A line 10 cm long is drawn to represent a distance of 3 km. To what scale is the line drawn?	1 cm to	300 m
6	POTATOES £1·40 for a 3-kg bag or 24p per $\frac{1}{2}$ kg How much money is saved by buying 6 kg potatoes in bags?		8p
7	A rectangular plot of ground measures 19.7 m long and 13.4 m wide. 'Round off' each measurement to the nearest m and then find the approximate area of the plot.		260 m²
8	Which of these shapes have two axes of symmetry?		B , E
9	There were three candidates A, B and C in an election. Of the total votes A polled $\frac{1}{4}$, B polled $\frac{1}{6}$ and C polled $\frac{1}{3}$. (a) Which candidate won the election?	(a)	C
	(b) What fraction of the electors did not vote?	(b)	$\frac{1}{4}$
10	The bottom of a rectangular tank measures 20 cm long and 10 cm wide. If 1 litre of water is poured into it, how deep is the water?		5 cm
11	The price of a pen was increased from 30p to 36p. Find the increase as a percentage.		20%
12	Find the greatest number of circles each with a diameter of 10 cm which can be marked out on a rectangular sheet of card 60 cm by 50 cm.		30

14

Section 1 Test 12

A

		ANSWER
1	1.4 million + 0.3 million	1.7 million
2	1000 × ▢ = 300	0.3
3	(a) 5% of £30	(a) £ 1·50
	(b) 40% of £50	(b) £ 20
4	2.050 ℓ − ▢ mℓ = $1\frac{1}{2}$ ℓ	550 mℓ
5	3x − x = 37 Find the value of x.	$18\frac{1}{2}$
6	6 × 9 × 5 × 4	1080
7	$\frac{4.56 \text{ m}}{8}$ = ▢ cm	57 cm
8	(a) 0.65 = ▢ % = $\frac{▢}{20}$ (a) 65% = $\frac{13}{20}$	
	(b) 0.12 = ▢ % = $\frac{3}{▢}$ (b) 12% = $\frac{3}{25}$	
9	7 h − 3 h 28 min = ▢ h ▢ min	3 h 32 min
10	1.34 + ▢ = 1.876	0.536
11	9.072 × 7	63.504
12	£5·00 ÷ 6 = ▢ p rem. ▢ p	83p rem. 2p

B

		ANSWER
1	Take the sum of $\frac{2}{3}$ and $\frac{5}{6}$ from 2.	$\frac{1}{2}$
2	How many times is 600 g contained in 4.8 kg?	8
3	£ 4 · 7 4 − ▢ · ▢ ▢ = 1 · 9 0 Find the missing sum of money.	£ 2·84
4	How many days inclusive from 23rd Nov. to 9th Dec.?	17
5	Find the reflex angle to an angle of 63°.	297°
6	To the total of 850 mℓ and 950 mℓ add 1.6 ℓ. Give the answer in ℓ.	3.4 ℓ
7	What percentage of (a) £400 is £20	(a) 5%
	(b) 1 tonne is 250 kg?	(b) 25%
8	What number when divided by 9 gives 3.68 as the answer?	33.12
9	40% of a sum of money is 60p. Find the whole amount.	£ 1·50
10	0.8 0.15 0.25 0.125	
	Which of these decimal fractions equals $\frac{1}{8}$?	0.125
11	Divide £10·00 by 3. Give the answer to the nearest penny.	£ 3·33
12	Find the circumference of the circle to the nearest cm. (C = 2πr; π = 3.14)	6 cm

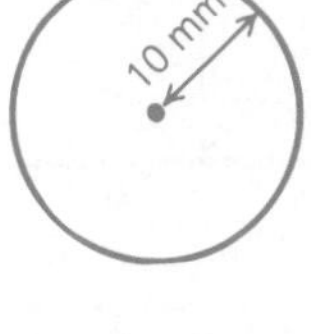

C

		ANSWER
1	By how many is (3 × 10⁴) less than fifty thousand?	20 000
2	The mass of a FIVE coin is 3.25 g. What is the value of the FIVES in a bag if their mass is 0.325 kg?	£ 5
3	Of 240 children in a school 180 stay for dinner. Find the percentage of children who go home for dinner.	25%
4	*[diagram: Alton — 2.6 km — peak — 1.4 km — dip — 3.9 km — Bigby]* Find to the nearest km the distance by road from Alton to Bigby.	8 km
5	The average temperature over four consecutive days was 17°C. For three of the days the temperatures were 16°, 14° and 18° respectively. What was the temperature on the fourth day?	20°C
6	Find the value of a when 3a + 4 = 31.	9
7	In this ready reckoner two of the prices, marked x and y, are missing. What are they?	

MASS	100 g	150 g	200 g	300 g	400 g
PRICE	18p	27p	x	54p	y

x 36p y 72p

8	A girl saves £7·50 in 5 months. If she continues to save at the same rate, how much will she have saved in (a) 7 months	(a) £ 10·50
	(b) 1 year?	(b) £ 18
9	*[diagram of shape: rectangle 8 cm and 15 cm with triangle, 12 cm]* (a) Name the kind of triangle which is added to the rectangle to make the shape.	(a) right-angled
	(b) Find the area of the shape.	(b) 150 cm²
10	The diameter of a wheel is 30 cm. (a) π = 3.14. Find the circumference of the wheel.	(a) 94.2 cm
	(b) Find to the nearest m the distance travelled for 100 turns of the wheel.	(b) 94 m
11	(a) How much is 18% of £1·00?	(a) 18p
	(b) Olivia puts a present of £20 in the bank for 1 year. How much interest does she receive at 11% per annum?	(b) £ 2·20
12	A fish tank is a cube of 20-cm side. Find in kg the mass of water in the tank when it is half full.	4 kg

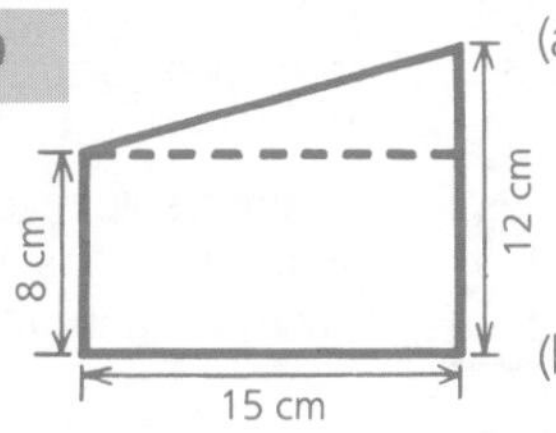

Next work Progress Test 1 on page 16.
Enter the result and the date on the chart.

PROGRESS TEST 1

Write the numbers 1 to 20 down the side of a sheet of paper.
Write alongside these numbers the **answers only** to the following questions.
Work as quickly as you can.
Time allowed − **10 minutes.**

1 Write in words the number which is equal to $(5 \times 10^4) + (7 \times 10) + 2$.

fifty thousand and seventy-two

2 How many times is 1083 greater than 1.083?

1000

3 How many FIVES are given in exchange for the coins shown in the box?

29 FIVES

4 $8.150 \, \ell - 800 \, m\ell$ Write the answer in ℓ.

7.350 ℓ

5 $\frac{x}{9} = 7.14$ Find the value of x.

64.26

6 By how many degrees is the angle marked x in the parallelogram less than the angle marked y ?

68°

7 The price of an article was increased from £20 to £25. What is the increase as a percentage of the original price?

25%

8 A line 8 cm long represents a distance of 3.2 m. The scale to which the line is drawn is 1 mm to ▓ cm.

1mm to 4 cm

9 Write as a mixed number the difference between 3 and 0.125.

$2\frac{7}{8}$

10 The packing material on a parcel is 5% of its gross mass which is 15 kg. Find in g the mass of the packing material.

750 g

11 Josh had £4·20. The diagram shows how he used it. How much money did he put into the savings bank?

£1·40

12 The number of people living in a small town was 19 097. In five years the population decreased by 10%. Find the decrease to the nearest whole one.

1910

13 The area of a triangle is 32.2 cm². Its height is 7 cm. Find the length of the base.

9.2 cm

14

	DEPART	ARRIVE
A	10.20	13.55
B	11.25	14.15

The timetable gives the times of two trains from London to Leeds. Which train is the quicker and by how many minutes?

B by 45 min

15 A pack of 8 cans of fruit juice costs £3·75. Find to the nearest penny the cost of one can.

47p

16 Beef steak costs £3·50 per $\frac{1}{2}$ kg. Find the cost of 1 kg 600 g.

£11·20

17 The perimeter of a rectangular hall is 36 m. The width measures one third of the length. Find the length of the hall.

13.5 m

18 $\frac{5}{6}$ of a sum of money is £10·40. What is the whole amount?

£12·48

19 A car travels at a speed of 45 km/h for 1 h and then at 60 km/h for 2 h. Find the average speed of the car.

55 km/h

20 The area of the bottom of this tin is 76.5 cm². Its height is 10 cm. What decimal fraction of 1 litre of water does the tin hold?

0.765 ℓ

PROGRESS TEST 1

You will work Progress Test 1 at **four** different times. When you first work the test
  (a) colour the first column to show the number of examples correct out of 20
  (b) enter the date.
Each time you work the test, enter the result and the date in the marked columns.

	1st	2nd	3rd	4th
20				
19				
18				
17				
16				
15				
14				
13				
12				
11				
10				
9				
8				
7				
6				
5				
4				
3				
2				
1				
0				
date				

number of examples correct

Section 2 Test 1

A

		ANSWER
1	Write in words the number shown on the abacus picture.	two hundred and thirty-five thousand and four hundred
2	Add 1.0, 0.1 and 0.001.	1.101
3	3375 mm = ▢ m	3.375 m
4	▢ × 10 = 498 700	49 870
5	£0·75 = 2 TWENTIES + 1 TEN + ▢ FIVES	5 FIVES
6	8 kg – 6.075 kg = ▢ kg	1.925 kg
7	6 × 5 × 9	270
8	$2\frac{1}{4}$ min = ▢ s	135 s
9	$\frac{3}{5}$ of £45 = £ ▢	£ 27
10	$\frac{3}{12} + \frac{1}{6}$	$\frac{5}{12}$
11	$3^3 - 2^3$	19
12	Find 15% of £2·00.	30p

B

		ANSWER
1	1 metre costs £1·50. Find the cost of 10 cm.	15p
2	Reduce $\frac{12}{16}$ to its lowest terms.	$\frac{3}{4}$
3	To the difference between £5·00 and £2·55 add 6 TWOS.	£ 2·57
4	A square has a perimeter of 320 mm. Find its area in cm².	64 cm²
5	How many times can 0.25 be taken from 1?	4
6	Write, using index notation, 4 × 4 × 4 × 4.	4^4
7	When a drum is $\frac{3}{4}$ full it holds 900 mℓ. How much in ℓ does it hold when it is full?	1.2 ℓ
8	What percentage of £6 is £1·50?	25%
9	Find the volume in m³ of a room 5 m long, 4 m wide and 2.5 m high.	50 m³
10	What fraction in its lowest terms is equal to 12.5% ?	$\frac{1}{8}$
11	How many times heavier is 7.5 kg than 75 g?	100
12	$\frac{2}{3}$ $\frac{3}{4}$ $\frac{7}{12}$ $\frac{5}{6}$ Write these fractions in order of size, the largest first.	$\frac{5}{6}, \frac{3}{4}, \frac{2}{3}, \frac{7}{12}$

C

		ANSWER
1	Six 30-cm rulers are placed end to end. How many mm short of 2 m is their total length?	200 mm
2	(a) 1676 (b) 1918 In which century did each of these years fall? Write the answers in figures.	(a) 17th (b) 20th
3	Find (a) the reflex angle Y (b) the acute angle Z.	(a) 251° (b) 75°
4	3 6 7 5 8 Write this number and use a decimal point to make the value of the number (a) between 360 and 370 (b) between 30 and 40.	(a) 367.58 (b) 36.758
5	Which number when divided by 6 has $\frac{1}{3}$ as the answer?	2
6	12 17 18 24 27 31 36 Which of these numbers have 2, 3 and 4 as factors?	12 , 24 , 36
7	ALL GOODS REDUCED 6p in the £ (a) Find the amount of the reduction on a pair of shoes costing £29·50. (b) What percentage is the reduction?	(a) £ 1·77 (b) 6 %
8	A plan is drawn to a scale of 1 mm to 10 cm. Write the scale as a fraction.	$\frac{1}{100}$
9	There are 24 small squares in the diagram. Find as a fraction in its lowest terms the part which is (a) shaded (b) unshaded (c) coloured.	(a) $\frac{2}{3}$ (b) $\frac{1}{8}$ (c) $\frac{5}{24}$
10	£5·75 £3·25 £2·99 'Round off' each amount to the nearest £ and then find the approximate total.	£ 12
11	The area of the circle from which the quadrant in the square is cut is 1256 cm². How much greater in cm² is the area of the square than that of the quadrant? (20 cm)	86 cm²
12	346 × 18 = 6228 Find (a) 346 × 0.18 (b) 34.6 × 1.8.	(a) 62.28 (b) 62.28

Section 2 Test 2

ANSWER

1	$4 \times y = 96$ Find the value of y.	24
2	£3·78 + £2·55	£ 6·33
3	35 min × 5 = ▢ h ▢ min	2 h 55 min
4	£ ▢ + £2·37 = £6·00	£ 3·63
5	1 tonne (t) = 1000 kg 3080 kg = ▢ t ▢ kg	3 t 80 kg
6	$2\frac{3}{8} - 1\frac{1}{4}$	$1\frac{1}{8}$
7	$4.804 = \frac{▢}{1000}$	$\frac{4804}{1000}$
8	(a) $\frac{1}{6}$ of 156	(a) 26
	(b) $\frac{1}{12}$ of 156	(b) 13
9	(a) 20p of £2·00 = ▢ %	(a) 10%
	(b) 20p of £4·00 = ▢ %	(b) 5%
10	$4^3 + 4^2$	80
11	5057 m + ▢ m = 5.750 km	693 m
12	$\frac{£3·50}{10} \times 3$	£ 1·05

B **ANSWER**

1	Write in figures seven hundred thousand seven hundred.	700 700
2	Increase the sum of 54p and 18p by £1·08.	£ 1·80
3	By how many mm is 2620 mm less than 3 m?	380 mm
4	One article cost 18p. Find the cost of (a) 10 (b) 30.	(a) £ 1·80
		(b) £ 5·40
5	▢ 50 5 0.5 ▢ ▢ ▢ Write the next two numbers in this series.	0.05 , 0.005
6	How many times is 300 g contained in 9 kg?	30
7	Write $\frac{3}{5}$ as a decimal fraction.	0.6
8	Increase (a) £1·00 by 13%	(a) £ 1·13
	(b) £1·00 by 9%.	(b) £ 1·09
9	▢ 16 14 17 13 ▢ Find the average of these numbers.	15
10	A rectangle is 4.5 m long and 0.5 m wide. Find (a) the perimeter	(a) 10 m
	(b) the area.	(b) 2.25 m²
	Write the unit of measurement in each case.	
11	Find the difference between 2.75 million and 300 000.	2 450 000
12	For the rectangle find ∠ a	∠ a 29°
	∠ b	∠ b 122°
	and ∠ c.	∠ c 61°

C **ANSWER**

1	What speed in km/h is (a) 6 km in 3 min	(a) 120 km/h
	(b) 72 km in 45 min?	(b) 96 km/h
2	Mr Khan was given 10% reduction on a car costing £3000. How much did he pay for the car?	£ 2700
3	Six jugs each holding 850 mℓ were filled from a cask containing 10 ℓ. Write in ℓ the quantity remaining.	4.900 ℓ
4	Estimate which of these angles is (a) 87° (b) 135°	(a) y (b) x
	(c) 278° (d) 45°.	(c) z (d) w
5	In a class of 32 children, 24 could swim. What percentage of the children could not swim?	25%
6	Find in mm (a) the total of the lengths AB and AC	(a) 82 mm
	(b) the difference in length between AB and AC.	(b) 28 mm
7	An article cost £1·00. An increase of 8p is added. What is the increase per cent?	8%
8	On parents' evening, 4 out of every 5 parents who attended were women. 100 parents attended. (a) How many were women?	(a) 80
	(b) What fraction were men?	(b) $\frac{1}{5}$
9	Area 7.5 m² 1.5 m Find the length of the rectangle in m.	5 m
10	A man works from 6.45 a.m. to 10.15 a.m. and from 3.15 p.m. to 6.45 p.m. How many hours is that each day?	7 h
11	The volume of the cuboid is 150 m³. Find its height in m. 5 m 4 m	7.5 m
12	A car travelled 50 106 km in 3 years. Find to the nearest 1000 km the distance travelled per year.	17 000 km

19

A

		ANSWER
1	£0·07 + £7·00 + £0·70	£ 7·77
2	$(7 \times 10^3) + (5 \times 10^2) + (3 \times 10^1)$	7530
3	▨ p × 10 = £1·60	16p
4	870 kg + 0.5 tonne = ▨ t	1.370 t
5	1.36 ÷ 8	0.17
6	(4 × 96) + (6 × 96)	960
7	360° − (145° + 55°)	160°
8	$3\,\ell\,250\,m\ell - \frac{3}{4}\ell = ▨\ \ell$	2.5 ℓ
9	3.593 + 0.407	4.0
10	80% of 400	320
11	$\frac{2}{3} + \frac{1}{6}$	$\frac{5}{6}$
12	$3 \times 3 = 3^2 = 9 \qquad \sqrt{9} = 3$ Find $\sqrt{36}$.	6

B

		ANSWER
1	What number is one more than 99 999?	100 000
2	By how many seconds is 70 s less than $1\frac{1}{4}$ minutes?	5 s
3	700 mℓ cost £0·91. Find the cost per litre.	£ 1·30
4	The length of a rectangle is 15 cm and its perimeter is 46 cm. Find (a) the width	(a) 8 cm
	(b) the area.	(b) 120 cm²
5	Write 1 mm of 2 m as (a) a fraction	(a) $\frac{1}{2000}$
	(b) a ratio.	(b) 1:2000
6	Divide the total of £1·17 and £0·28 by 5.	£ 0·29
7	4 × y = 4y Find the value of y when 4y = 14.	$3\frac{1}{2}$
8	Approximate (a) 9493 g to the nearest kg	(a) 9 kg
	(b) 305 426 to the nearest 10 000.	(b) 310 000
9	Write as a decimal the sum of 5, $\frac{3}{10}$ and $\frac{84}{100}$.	6.14
10	What percentage is 6 cm of 2 m?	3%
11	$\begin{array}{\|c\|c\|c\|c\|c\|c\|c\|} \hline \frac{1}{10} & \frac{1}{5} & \frac{3}{10} & \frac{2}{5} & \frac{1}{2} & & \\ \hline \end{array}$ Write the next two numbers in this series.	$\frac{3}{5}$, $\frac{7}{10}$
12	Write 125 mℓ of 1 litre as (a) a fraction in its lowest terms	(a) $\frac{1}{8}$
	(b) a decimal fraction.	(b) 0.125

C

		ANSWER
1	The price of a 32p packet of sweets is increased by 25%. What is the new price?	40p
2	AIR SHOW ADMISSION £4·20 Children: half-price Find the total cost for 2 adults and 2 children.	£ 12·60
3	The length of a garage is 5 metres. The overall length of a car is 4445 mm. By how many mm is the garage longer than the car?	555 mm
4	A woman is employed for 36 hours from Monday to Friday (inclusive). Find in h and min the average time she works each day.	7 h 12 min
5	From a gift of £10. Ahmed received £3·70. His three sisters shared the remainder equally. How much did each sister receive.	£ 2·10
6	A packet of weed-killer will treat 100 m² of lawn. How many packets are needed to treat a square lawn with 20-m sides?	4
7	Two of the angles in each of the triangles X, Y and Z are given. Find the third angle for each triangle.	

Triangle X	96°	42°	▨ °	X			42°
Triangle Y	60°	60°	▨ °	Y			60°
Triangle Z	90°	57°	▨ °	Z			33°

		ANSWER
8	A map is drawn to a scale of 1 cm to 1 km (1:100 000). Find the distance in km represented by a line 42 mm long.	4.2 km
9	F = { 16 4 ▨ 1 64 2 ▨ } F = the set of factors of 64. Find the missing factors.	8 , 32
10	How many litres of water can be contained in a tank measuring (a) 10 cm long, 10 cm wide, 10 cm high	(a) 1 ℓ
	(b) 30 cm long, 20 cm wide, 30 cm high?	(b) 18 ℓ
11	The squares of the grid have 5-mm sides. Find the area of the shaded triangle in cm².	3 cm²
12	Net mass 2 kg 100 g The mass of the contents of the box is $\frac{7}{8}$ of the total mass. Find in kg the gross mass.	2.400 kg

Section 2   Test 4

A

		ANSWER
1	(4 × 9²)	324
2	0.9 − 0.09	0.81
3	15p × 4 = £	£ 0·60
4	3694 ÷ 5 = ▢ rem. ▢	738 rem. 4
5	(a) 0.12 = ▢ %	(a) 12 %
	(b) 0.125 = ▢ %	(b) 12.5 %
6	2 ℓ − ▢ mℓ = 1.260 ℓ	740 mℓ
7	$\frac{1}{8}$ of 360°	45°
8	1 m 90 mm = ▢ m	1.090 m
9	3 FIFTIES + ▢ FIVES = £3·00 − £1·25	5 FIVES
10	11.33 a.m. to 1.27 p.m. = ▢ h ▢ min	1 h 54 min
11	0.3 × 0.5	0.15
12	Find (a) $\frac{1}{2}$ of $\frac{2}{3}$	(a) $\frac{1}{3}$
	(b) $\frac{7}{8}$ of 4.	(b) $3\frac{1}{2}$

B

		ANSWER
1	How much is left when £1·67 is subtracted from £2·45?	£ 0·78
2	Write as a decimal fraction (a) $\frac{1}{4}$	(a) 0.25
	(b) $\frac{1}{8}$.	(b) 0.125
3	Write the volume in cm³ of a container which holds 2.250 ℓ.	2250 cm³
4	Find the difference between 100% of £5·00 and 1% of £5·00.	£ 4·95
5	What number is one thousand less than 800 000?	799 000
6	10 articles cost £4·50. Find the cost of (a) 1	(a) 45p
	(b) 7.	(b) £ 3·15
7	How many times can 300 mℓ be taken from 6 ℓ?	20
8	Which two consecutive numbers have a product of 72?	8 9
9	How many days inclusive from 14th December to 17th January?	35
10	Divide £5·00 by 9 to the nearest penny.	56p
11	ABCD is a parallelogram. Find in degrees ∠x	∠x 115°
	and ∠y.	∠y 65°
12	20% of a sum of money is 85p. What is the whole amount?	£ 4·25

C

		ANSWER
1	A jug holds 750 mℓ. How many mℓ does it hold when it is $\frac{2}{3}$ full?	500 mℓ
2	The interior angles of triangles A, B and C are given. Name each of the triangles by its sides.	

Triangle A	60°	60°	60°	A equilateral
Triangle B	80°	80°	20°	B isosceles
Triangle C	30°	60°	90°	C scalene

		ANSWER
3	A worker charges £4·00 per hour. How much is charged for 3 h 15 min?	£ 13·00
4	5.109 6.5 4.49 2.73	
	'Round off' each of the above to the nearest whole number and then find the approximate total.	19
5	The diagram shows how the children voted for their favourite sport. What percentage of the children voted for (a) swimming	(a) 25 %
	(b) cycling?	(b) 12.5 %
6	If 200 children voted, how many more voted for football than for cricket?	75
7	The area of the circle is 78.5 m². Find the area of the shaded sector.	15.7 m²
8	Eight lengths each measuring 2 m 40 cm are cut from a 20-m roll. What length in cm remains?	80 cm
9	When full the tank holds 10 000 cm³. (a) Find its depth.	(a) 10 cm
	(b) How many ℓ does it hold when full?	(b) 10 ℓ
10	In a freestyle swimming competition, George swam 200 m in 1 min 54.3 s. How many seconds less than 2 min was his time?	5.7 s
11	The diagram shows the distances between friends' homes. How many m is it from Sita's to Ellie's?	510 m
12	The population of a town of 0.5 million fell by 50 000. What was the percentage fall in population?	10 %

Turn back to page 16 and work for the second time Progress Test 1.
Enter the result and the date on the chart.

Section 2   Test 5

A

		ANSWER
1	36 mm + 24 mm + 54 mm = ▨ cm	11.4 cm
2	5 ℓ − (480 mℓ × 5) = ▨ ℓ	2.600 ℓ
3	▨ g × 100 = 6.5 kg	65 g
4	$(9 \times 10^4) + (8 \times 10^3) + (2 \times 1)$	98 002
5	2.750 ℓ ÷ 2	1.375 ℓ
6	60% of £2 = £ ▨	£ 1·20
7	0.97 × 3	2.91
8	3 h 50 min × 6 = ▨ h ▨ min	23 h 0 min
9	Find $\sqrt{64}$.	8
10	$9^3 - 9$	720
11	£30 ÷ 20	£ 1·50
12	£0·50 × 54	£ 27·00

B

		ANSWER
1	Write in words the number 40 400.	forty thousand four hundred
2	An aircraft flying North turned clockwise through 270°. In what direction was it then flying?	W
3	Divide £28 in the ratio 4:3.	£ 16 £ 12
4	6 articles cost 90p. Find the cost of 5 articles.	75p
5	Approximate (a) 0.830 km to the nearest 100 m	(a) 800 m
	(b) 4.080 ℓ to the nearest half litre.	(b) 4 ℓ
6	(a) How many 8-cm lengths can be cut from a 5-m length?	(a) 62
	(b) How many cm are left over?	(b) 4 cm
7	What fraction of 10 is $1\frac{1}{4}$?	$\frac{1}{8}$
8	Write as a decimal fraction (a) 19%	(a) 0.19
	(b) $12\frac{1}{2}$%.	(b) 0.125
9	Decrease £15·00 by 2%.	£ 14·70
10	6 + x + 0.029 = 6.030 Find x.	0.001
11	Find in mm the circumference of a circle with a radius of 50 mm. (π = 3.14)	314 mm
12	5 . 3 7 0 kg Find the missing − ▨ . ▨ ▨ ▨ kg mass in g. ———————— 4 . 4 9 0 kg	880 g

C

		ANSWER
1	20p is saved each week. How long will it take to save £2·60?	13 weeks
2	Find in m the perimeter of this square. ($1\frac{3}{4}$ m)	7 m
3	$\frac{1}{2}$ $\frac{1}{8}$ $\frac{1}{4}$ $\frac{1}{3}$ $\frac{1}{6}$ Which of these fractions is equal to (a) $12\frac{1}{2}$% (b) $33\frac{1}{3}$% ?	(a) $\frac{1}{8}$ (b) $\frac{1}{3}$
4	Find the difference between 30 × 4p and 30 times 6p.	60p
5	W X Y Z is a trapezium. Find in degrees (a) ∠ XYZ (b) ∠ YZW. (117° 117°)	(a) 63° (b) 63°
6	Of the 300 people employed at a factory 99% were present. How many people was that?	297
7	Tom was allowed an average of 50p per day spending money for 4 days. Find how much he had to spend on the fourth day.	30p

DAY	1st	2nd	3rd	4th
Spent	70p	40p	60p	

		ANSWER
8	From Aberdeen to Leicester by road is approximately 700 km. Find to the nearest h the time taken by a truck if the average speed is 60 km/h.	12 h
9	The scale is taken from a map. Find the distance in km represented by a line on the map measuring 3.5 cm.	17.5 km
10	An equilateral triangle has a perimeter of 240 mm. Find in cm (a) the length of one side	(a) 8 cm
	(b) the length of one side of a regular hexagon of the same perimeter.	(b) 4 cm
11	From this calendar find (a) the number of Fridays in the month	(a) 4
	(b) the date of the third Sunday in the month.	(b) 20th
12	Which is the better buy per kg and by how much? Y a 5-kg pack costing 75p Z a 1250-g pack costing 20p	Y by 1p

mm ruler scale: km 5 10 15 20 25 30

MARCH calendar:

MARCH					
Mon		7	14	21	28
Tues	1	8	15	22	29
Wed	2	9	16	23	30
Thurs	3	10	17	24	31

Section 2   Test 6

A

		ANSWER
1	470 − 383	87
2	250 g × 20 = ▨ kg	5 kg
3	765 ÷ 25 = ▨ rem. ▨	30 rem. 15
4	$2\frac{5}{8} + \frac{3}{4}$	$3\frac{3}{8}$
5	1 ÷ 0.2	5
6	4 m − ▨ mm = 3.180 m	820 mm
7	30 × 1.6	48
8	From 7.19 a.m. to 8.15 a.m. = ▨ min	56 min
9	175 mℓ × 4 = 1 ℓ − ▨ mℓ	300 mℓ
10	3y + 4 = 25 Find the value of y.	7
11	(a) 8.5% of £100	(a) £ 8·50
	(b) $12\frac{1}{2}$ % of £10	(b) £ 1·25
12	£2·63 × 4	£ 10·52

B

		ANSWER
1	0.099 0.9 0.909 0.09 Add together the largest and the smallest of these numbers.	0.999
2	What percentage is (a) 9 of 18	(a) 50 %
	(b) 18 of 9?	(b) 200 %
3	Write in figures the number which is ten thousand more than a million.	1 010 000
4	£2·57 plus £1·36 minus 24p = £ ▨	£ 3·69
5	Write 20 thirds as (a) an improper fraction	(a) $\frac{20}{3}$
	(b) a mixed number.	(b) $6\frac{2}{3}$
6	Find the area of a parallelogram of base 24.4 cm and height 50 cm.	1220 cm²
7	$\frac{1}{9}$ of 70. Write the answer to the nearest whole one.	8
8	50 g cost 65p. Find the cost of $\frac{1}{4}$ kg.	£ 3·25
9	How many 650-g packets can be made from 65 kg?	100
10	Write as a decimal fraction (a) $\frac{9}{50}$	(a) 0.18
	(b) $\frac{3}{20}$	(b) 0.15
	(c) $\frac{3}{25}$.	(c) 0.12
11	Find the difference in g between 1% of 19 kg and 1% of 20 kg.	10 g
12	Increase £2·00 by 16%.	£ 2·32

C

		ANSWER
1	To rent a video recorder costs £150 per year. How much is this per month?	£ 12·50
2	ABC is a right-angled triangle. Find its area.	17.5 cm²
3	Mr Jones paid 30% deposit on a carpet costing £150. How much more money had he to pay?	£ 105
4	A $2\frac{1}{2}$-ℓ container is $\frac{7}{10}$ full. What decimal fraction of 1 ℓ is required to fill it?	0.75 ℓ
5	A Scout group walked West for 5 km, North for 5 km and then East for 5 km. In which direction must they walk to get back to base by the shortest distance?	South
6		BROTON	CANT	WITTON	From this bus	 	19.17	21.14	23.56	timetable find the time taken from (a) Broton to Cant	(a) 1 h 57 min
	(b) Cant to Witton	(b) 2 h 42 min
	(c) Broton to Witton.	(c) 4 h 39 min
7	A new pane of glass is to be fitted into this square window. (a) In how many different ways will it fit without the glass being turned over?	(a) 4
	(b) How many lines of symmetry has a square?	(b) 4
8	$\left\{\frac{3}{5} \quad \frac{6}{10} \quad \frac{x}{15} \quad \frac{12}{20} \quad \frac{y}{25} \quad \frac{z}{30}\right\}$ Find the missing numerators x, y and z in this set of equivalent fractions.	x 9 y 15 z 18
9	The triangle is equilateral. Find in degrees the measurement of ∠ x	∠ x 120°
	and ∠ y.	∠ y 120°
10	A car averaged 8 km to a litre of petrol on a 4-hour journey of 312 km. (a) How many litres were used on the journey?	(a) 39 ℓ
	(b) What was the average speed?	(b) 78 km/h
11	(π = 3.14) The radius of the wheel is 25 cm. How far, in cm, will it travel in one complete turn?	157 cm
12	'Round-off' the sum of money to the nearest £ and then find an approximate answer. (a) £19·87 × 19	(a) £ 380
	(b) £126·24 ÷ 9	(b) £ 14

23

Section 2 Test 7

A

		ANSWER
1	5.384 + 4.16	9.544
2	4 km − 272 m = km	3.728 km
3	£30 × 27	£ 810
4	$\frac{£5·18}{6}$ = p rem. p	86 p rem. 2 p
5	1.5 million = thousands	1500 thousands
6	$(6 \times 10^5) + (1 \times 10^4) +$ $(7 \times 10^2) + (4 \times 1)$	610 704
7	0.75 ℓ = cm³	750 cm³
8	1.200 kg ÷ y = 150 g Find the value of y.	8
9	$\frac{y}{7}$ = 4.75 Find the value of y.	33.25
10	Find $\frac{3}{8}$ of £36.	£ 13·50
11	$\frac{48\text{ mm} + 72\text{ mm}}{4}$ = cm	3 cm
12	(a) 25% of 1.280 ℓ = mℓ	(a) 320 mℓ
	(b) 75% of 1.280 kg = g	(b) 960 g

B

		ANSWER
1	Divide $7\frac{1}{2}$ kg in the ratio 7:8.	$3\frac{1}{2}$ kg 4 kg
2	Find the product of 10 and 0.002.	0.02
3	One article costs 21p. Find the cost of (a) 10	(a) £ 2·10
	(b) 50.	(b) £ 10·50
4	$\boxed{\text{1 hectare (ha) = 10 000 m}^2}$ Find in ha the area of a field 100 m long and 200 m wide.	2 ha
5	(a) Increase £2·56 by 100%.	(a) £ 5·12
	(b) Decrease £2·40 by 50%.	(b) £ 1·20
6	By how many g is twice 2.175 kg less than 5 kg?	650 g
7	How many seconds in (a) 0.6 min	(a) 36 s
	(b) 0.25 min?	(b) 15 s
8	£5·60 is shared equally among 8 children. Find one share.	70 p
9	Change to percentages (a) 0.13	(a) 13%
	(b) 0.35.	(b) 35%
10	The area of a square card is 1 m². Find in cm the length of one side.	100 cm
11	0.75 of a quantity has a mass of 3.360 kg. Find the mass of 0.5 of the quantity.	2.240 kg
12	Find the sum of (4 × 2.54) and (2.54 × 6).	25.4

C

		ANSWER
1	A book was purchased for £2·40 and sold at a profit of 25%. What was the selling price?	£ 3·00
2	The total mass of the three parcels is 7 kg. Find in kg the mass of parcel C.	1.075 kg
3	Josh earns £5·50 per hour. What is his wage for a 30-hour week?	£ 165
4	The scale reading shows the mass of 20 tomatoes. Find the average mass of one tomato.	45 g
5	Find the change from £10 after spending £3·60, £2·50 and 99p.	£ 2·91
6	The right-angled triangle is an isosceles triangle. Find in degrees (a) ∠ CAB	(a) 45°
	(b) ∠ BCA.	(b) 45°
7	A packet of peas has a mass of 375 g. Find in kg the mass of six packets.	2.250 kg
8	The bottom of a rectangular container is 20 cm long and 10 cm wide. Two litres of water are poured into the container. Find the depth of water in cm.	10 cm
9	The perimeter of the rhombus is 80 mm. What is the area in mm² of the shaded triangle?	100 mm²
10	A measurement of 38 mm on a plan represents a distance of 38 m. Write the scale as (a) a fraction in its lowest terms	(a) $\frac{1}{1000}$
	(b) a ratio.	(b) 1:1000
11	The graph shows the temperature for 5 days. Find the average daily temperature.	6°C
12	$\boxed{\quad \frac{1}{4} \quad \frac{3}{8} \quad \frac{1}{5} \quad \frac{2}{3} \quad \frac{3}{10} \quad \frac{1}{12} \quad}$ Which two of these fractions together equal (a) $\frac{1}{2}$	(a) $\frac{1}{5}$ and $\frac{3}{10}$
	(b) $\frac{3}{4}$?	(b) $\frac{2}{3}$ and $\frac{1}{12}$

Section 2 Test 8

A

		ANSWER
1	$79 + 87 + \boxed{} = 300$	134
2	$10^6 = 10 \times 10 \times 10 \times 10 \times 10 \times 10 = \boxed{}$	1 000 000
3	$3\text{ h }20\text{ min} - 1\text{ h }55\text{ min} = \boxed{}\text{ h }\boxed{}\text{ min}$	1 h 25 min
4	$6\,\ell\,515\text{ m}\ell = \boxed{}\text{ m}\ell$	6515 mℓ
5	£10·10 × 10	£ 101·00
6	$0.750\text{ m} + 350\text{ mm} + 400\text{ mm} = \boxed{}\text{ m}$	1.5 m
7	$9.18 + \boxed{}\text{ hundredths} = 10$	82 hundredths
8	36 × 6p	£ 2·16
9	6% of $\frac{1}{2}$ kg = $\boxed{}$ g	30 g
10	$10^3 - 87$	913
11	7 kg ÷ 8 = $\boxed{}$ g	875 g
12	$y \div 5 = \frac{2}{5}$ Find the value of y.	2

B

		ANSWER
1	Write in figures the number one hundred and eleven thousand and one.	111 001
2	How much less than 1 tonne is 860 kg?	140 kg
3	How many £s are equal in value to 10 000p?	£ 100
4	Which three consecutive numbers when added together equal 21?	6 7 8
5	Find (a) 1% of £75·00	(a) 75p
	(b) 11% of £75·00.	(b) £ 8·25
6	20 cost £8. Find the cost of 15.	£ 6
7	Write 300 mℓ of 0.5 ℓ as (a) a fraction in its lowest terms	(a) $\frac{3}{5}$
	(b) a percentage	(b) 60%
	(c) a ratio.	(c) 3:5
8	When $y = 2$, $6y = w - 8$. Find the value of w.	20
9	How many 400-g packs can be filled from 10 kg?	25
10	Write as a decimal (a) $\frac{3}{8}$	(a) 0.375
	(b) $\frac{7}{8}$.	(b) 0.875
11	Write the numbers between 0 and 40 of which both 3 and 4 are factors.	12 , 24 , 36
12	The length of a rectangle is twice its width. The perimeter is 54 cm. Find (a) the length	(a) 18 cm
	(b) the width.	(b) 9 cm

C

		ANSWER
1	6% of a 4-metre roll of ribbon was used. How many cm was that?	24 cm
2	Posts are erected at 100-m intervals on a motorway. How many posts are there in a distance of 4.700 km?	48
3	Four hinges together have a mass of 200 g. How many have a mass of $2\frac{1}{2}$ kg?	50
4	Find to the nearest whole number (a) $\frac{51}{4}$	(a) 13
	(b) 97 ÷ 8	(b) 12
	(c) 156.6 ÷ 6.	(c) 26
5	ABCD is a square. E is the mid point of the side AB. Find in degrees the size of each of the angles x, y and z.	$\angle x$ 63° $\angle y$ 54° $\angle z$ 27°
6	£3·52 was received in change from £10 after buying 6 plants. Find the average cost of a plant.	£ 1·08
7	A plan which measures 50 cm long and 20 cm wide is drawn to a scale of 1 cm to 2 m (1:200). Find the area in m² represented by the plan.	4000 m²
8	The circumference of the circle is 420 mm. Find the length of the arcs of (a) sector Y	(a) 42 mm
	(b) sector Z.	(b) 70 mm
9	Find the cost of 2.250 kg at 30p per $\frac{1}{2}$ kg.	£ 1·35
10	How many cubes of side 10 cm fit into a cube of side 1 metre?	1000
11	The drawing is an enlargement of part of the dial of a stop-watch which measures to one-tenth of a second. (a) Write in seconds the reading at Y	(a) Y 10.9 s
	at Z.	Z 12.3 s
	(b) Write in s the difference between the readings at Y and Z.	(b) 1.4 s
12	In 4 weeks a man travelled 530 km, 470 km, 640 km and 360 km. What was the average distance he travelled per week?	500 km

Turn back to page 16 and work for the third time Progress Test 1. Enter the result and the date on the chart.

Section 2   Test 9

A

		ANSWER
1	$700\,000 + \boxed{} + 2000 + 50 = 712\,050$	10 000
2	$8.5 - 7.05$	1.45
3	$2\frac{3}{4} \times 100$	275
4	$98° + 134° + \boxed{}° = 360°$	128°
5	$£ \boxed{} \times 4 = £15·24$	£ 3·81
6	$3.079 + \boxed{}$ thousandths $= 4$	921 thousandths
7	$(£1·08 \times 10) + (£0·07 \times 6)$	£ 11·22
8	$\frac{78}{x} = 3$ Find the value of x.	26
9	$34.86 = 10 \times \boxed{}$	3.486
10	$(56 \div 8) + (5.6 \div 0.8)$	14
11	$1160\,g \times 5 = \boxed{}$ kg	5.800 kg
12	From 6.12.'02 to 18.1.'03 inclusive $= \boxed{}$ days	44 days

B

		ANSWER
1	Write 10 532 thousandths as a decimal.	10.532
2	How much less than 10 tonnes is 9 t 470 kg?	530 kg
3	Find the sum of 1^4 and 2^3.	9
4	Find in °C the difference between (a) 6°C and -3°C	(a) 9°C
	(b) -5°C and 4°C.	(b) 9°C
5	Divide 117 by 8. Write the answer as a mixed number.	$14\frac{5}{8}$
6	Find the total of $(4 \times 16 \times 0)$ and $(4 \times 16 \times 1)$.	64
7	What is the interest on £250 for 1 year at 8% ?	£ 20
8	The area of a rectangle is 1 m². The breadth is 50 cm. Find the length in m.	2 m
9	10 articles cost £2·70. Find the cost of 3.	81p
10	Write 12 kg of 80 kg (a) as a fraction in its lowest terms	(a) $\frac{3}{20}$
	(b) as a percentage.	(b) 15%
11	How many km and m are equal to 0.75 of 6 km?	4 km 500 m
12		2.1 kg 0.75 kg 2.25 kg 4.9 kg	
	Find in kg the average mass.	2.5 kg

C

		ANSWER
1	ABCD is a quadrilateral. Find ∠ ABC.	69°
2	How many 40-cm lengths can be cut from a 10-m roll of tape?	25
3	Using a scale of 1 mm to 15 cm, what length of line would represent 3 m?	20 mm
4	The correct time is 12.05 a.m. How many minutes fast or slow is each of the 24-hour clocks? Y 18 min fast	
		Z 21 min slow
5	600 sheets of paper are used from 5 packs each holding 480 sheets. How many sheets are left?	1800
6	The diagram is a plan of a field. Find the area of the field in (a) m² (a) 30 000 m²	
	(b) ha. (b) 3.0 ha	
7	$P = \{7, x, y, 17, z, 23\}$ $P =$ the set of prime numbers between 6 and 24. Find the value of x, y and z.	x 11
		y 13
		z 19
8	There are 65 litres of diesel oil in a tractor tank. If the fuel is used at the rate of 15 ℓ per hour, for how many h and min can the tractor be used? 4 h 20 min	
9		length	24 cm	12 cm	The area of the two given rectangles is 24 cm².	

length	24 cm	12 cm
breadth	1 cm	2 cm

Find the length and breadth of two other rectangles X and Y each of which has an area of 24 cm².

X	6 cm	4 cm
Y	8 cm	3 cm

10	A roll of material 2.5 m long is cut into 3 equal pieces. Find to the nearest cm the length of one piece.	83 cm
11	The cylinder holds 2 litres. (a) How many mℓ of water are there in the cylinder? (a) 1200 mℓ	
	(b) How many more mℓ are required to fill it? (b) 800 mℓ	
12	Find the change from £10 after spending £2·46, £3·77 and £1·54.	£ 2·23

26

Section 2 Test 10

A | ANSWER

1	$(8 \times 10^6) + (2 \times 10^4) +$ (4×10^2)	8 020 400
2	$1000 \times \boxed{} = 59$	0.059
3	£$\frac{48}{100} = \boxed{}$ p	48p
4	$2\frac{5}{8} + \frac{3}{10} + 1\frac{3}{8}$	$4\frac{3}{10}$
5	9 kg = 7.355 kg + $\boxed{}$ kg	1.645 kg
6	$0.04 + 0.7 + 0.009 =$ $\boxed{}$ thousandths	749 thousandths
7	£0·09 × 12	£ 1·08
8	(a) 7% of £13·00	(a) 91p
	(b) 19% of £8·00	(b) £ 1·52
9	557 mℓ × 6 = $\boxed{}$ ℓ	3.342 ℓ
10	$\frac{1 \text{ kg } 350 \text{ g} \times 2}{10} = \boxed{}$ g	270 g
11	£5·00 − (£2·46 + £1·59)	95p
12	0.01 of 3.5 ℓ = $\boxed{}$ mℓ	35 mℓ

B | ANSWER

1	30 articles cost £2·40. Find the cost of 1.	8p
2	x y 53.057 — How many times smaller is the 5 marked y than the 5 marked x?	1000
3	From the sum of £4·65 and £3·35 subtract £5·50.	£ 2·50
4	Find the difference in cm between 153 mm and 6.6 cm.	8.7 cm
5	Approximate (a) 15 cm 7 mm to the nearest 0.5 cm	15.5 cm
	(b) 9 kg 75 g to the nearest 0.5 kg.	9 kg
6	Find the product of $1\frac{2}{3}$ and 30.	50
7	In how many years will the interest on £100 at 6% amount to £12?	2
8	Find the difference between (17 × 10) and (1.7 × 10).	153
9	Write $\frac{21}{50}$ as a decimal fraction.	0.42
10	The area of a carpet is 58.5 m². The length is 9 m. Find the width.	6.5 m
11	20 ℓ of a liquid is poured in equal amounts into 50 bottles. How many mℓ are there in each?	400 mℓ
12	An aircraft travels 1 km in 5 seconds. Find its speed in km/h.	720 km/h

C | ANSWER

1	Ryan spent £1·40 which was $\frac{5}{6}$ of his money. How much had he at first?	£ 1·68
2	A family of 4 drink 2.5 litres of milk each day. What is the average amount in mℓ for each person?	625 mℓ
3	Sean's salary is £795.63 a month. 'Round off' this amount to the nearest £10 and then find his approximate annual salary.	£ 9600
4	John Brown was born in 1883 and died in 1967. How old was he when he died?	84

5

Net mass	450 g	1.75 kg	z kg
Mass of box	x g	750 g	150 kg
Gross mass	635 g	y kg	1.1 t

Find each missing mass.

x	185 g
y	2.5 kg
z	950 kg

6

Fish	£2·60
Sweet	£0·70
Roll	£0·20

8% was added to this bill. Find the total amount to be paid. £ 3·78

7	Pins cost 6p for 10. How many pins can be bought for £1·14? — 190

8

W	X	Y
78°	60°	40°
	71°	90°
51°		

Two of the angles in each of the triangles W, X and Y are given. Find the third angle in each triangle.

W	51°
X	49°
Y	50°

9

09.00 – 10.00	10.00 – 11.00	11.00 – 12.00
85 km	110 km	75 km

The chart shows the distances travelled by a motorist in 3 hours. Find his average speed in km/h. 90 km/h

10	The scale of a map is 1:10 000. What distance in metres is represented on the map by (a) 1 mm	(a) 10 m
	(b) 3.5 cm?	(b) 350 m

11	The shape is divided into a rectangle and a triangle. Find the area of (a) the triangle	(a) 12.5 cm²
	(b) the whole shape.	(b) 62.5 cm²

10 cm, 5 cm, 15 cm

12	The volume of the cuboid is 175 cm³. Find its length. Area 25 cm²	7 cm

Section 2   Test 11

A

		ANSWER
1	3 FIFTIES and 13 TENS = £	£ 2·80
2	$5\ell \div 4 = $ ml	1250 mℓ
3	4 h 27 min + 2 h 35 min	7 h 2 min
4	6% of 500 mℓ	30 mℓ
5	3.750 m − 2800 mm = mm	950 mm
6	1.12 ÷ 8	0.14
7	$14 - 5\frac{3}{8}$	$8\frac{5}{8}$
8	$7x + 8 = 36$ Find the value of x.	4
9	$y\,)\overline{5.250}$ $\dfrac{0.250}{}$ Find the value of y.	21
10	Write as decimal fractions (a) 23%	(a) 0.23
	(b) $\frac{3}{15}$.	(b) 0.2
11	0.25 million + 6700	256 700
12	£ ÷ 7 = £2·67	£ 18·69

B

		ANSWER
1	Subtract half of £4·36 from £5.	£ 2·82
2	Find in ℓ the total of 375 mℓ, 0.325 ℓ and 0.250 ℓ.	0.950 ℓ
3	Find in mm $\frac{7}{10}$ of 8 cm.	56 mm
4	Multiply 50 by $1\frac{4}{5}$.	90
5	What distance is travelled in 40 min walking at an average speed of 6 km/h?	4 km
6	Write as a percentage (a) 30p of £2	(a) 15%
	(b) 30p of £4.	(b) 7.5%
7	1 metre of cloth costs £6. Find the cost of 90 cm.	£ 5·40
8	How many thousandths have the same value as 16 hundredths?	160 thousandths
9	Write 5 cm of 10 m (a) as a fraction in its lowest terms	(a) $\frac{1}{200}$
	(b) as a ratio.	(b) 1:200
10	Find the difference between 100 times £0·36 and 1000 times £0·36.	£ 324
11	(a) Write as a decimal to the nearest tenth $9\frac{37}{100}$.	(a) 9.4
	(b) Write to the first decimal place 8.64.	(b) 8.6
12	π = 3.14 The circumference of a circle is 314 mm. Find the diameter.	100 mm

C

		ANSWER
1	Write as a fraction in its lowest terms (a) 2p of 10p (b) 5p of £1	(a) $\frac{1}{5}$ (b) $\frac{1}{20}$
2	Calculate angle x	∠ x 88°
	angle y.	∠ y 135°
3	Find the total mass of 50 packets each having a mass of 3.560 kg.	178 kg
4	A worker pays £9·00 per week for meals at a factory. The price of a meal is to be increased by 5%. How much will then be paid?	£ 9·45
5	09998.7 This is a reading of the number of km travelled by a car. How many km short of 10 000 km has the car travelled?	1.3 km
6	Share £27·50 in the ratio of 2:3.	£ 11 £ 16·50
7	Which of the triangles X, Y or Z has (X isosceles, Y scalene, Z equilateral)	
	(a) 3 lines of symmetry	(a) Z
	(b) 1 line of symmetry	(b) X
	(c) no line of symmetry?	(c) Y
8	10 articles cost £1·40. Find the cost of 25.	£ 3·50
9	Find the area of this shape in mm².	500 mm²
10	0.9 × 10 10 × 0.99 1.9 × 10 10 × 0.09 10 × 9.9	
	For which of the examples above is (a) 100 the best approximation	(a) 10 × 9.9
	(b) 10 the best approximation?	(b) 10 × 0.99
11	Tom delivers newspapers on each of 6 days. The deliveries take 55 min each day. He is paid 80p per hour. How much does he earn each week?	£ 4·40
12	A water tank has a volume of one cubic metre. Find (a) its volume in cm³	(a) 1 000 000 cm³
	(b) the mass of the water in kg.	(b) 1000 kg

Turn back to page 16 and work for the fourth time Progress Test 1. Enter the result and the date on the chart.

Section 2   Test 12

A

			ANSWER
1	$2 \times 34 \times 5$		340
2	£3·73 + £1·17 + 90p = £		£ 5·80
3	86 360 ÷ 50 = 1727 rem.		10
4	855 g + g = 1.250 kg		395 g
5	(a) 86p = % of £1	(a)	86%
	(b) 50p = % of £5	(b)	10%
6	$\frac{232}{8} = x$ Find the value of x.		29
7	3.5 ℓ − (750 mℓ × 4) = mℓ		500 mℓ
8	$20\overline{)\,y\,}^{\,7.5}$ Find the value of y.		150
9	200×0.018		3.6
10	8.610 t ÷ 7 = kg		1230 kg
11	£10 − (£2·27 × 3)		£ 3·19
12	$(6 \times 0.5) - (7 \times 0.25)$		1.25

B

			ANSWER
1	Write 77 ÷ 8 as (a) an improper fraction	(a)	$\frac{77}{8}$
	(b) a mixed number.	(b)	$9\frac{5}{8}$
2	A booklet is 1.8 mm thick. What would be the height of a pile of (a) 5 booklets	(a)	9 mm
	(b) 15 booklets?	(b)	27 mm
3	How many days inclusive from 19th October to 6th November?		19
4	How many thousands in a quarter of a million?	250 thousands	
5	How many articles costing 2p each can be bought for £5·90?		295
6	One can contains 1.250 ℓ and another 950 mℓ. Find in ℓ the average contents.	1.100 ℓ	
7	Write as a decimal (a) 850 g of 1 kg	(a)	0.850
	(b) 730 mℓ of 1 ℓ.	(b)	0.730
8	The height of a triangle is 20 cm and the area is 160 cm². Find the length of the base.		16 cm
9	Divide the total of £3·87 and £4·33 by 4.		£ 2·05
10	Write as a decimal (a) $\frac{9}{20}$	(a)	0.45
	(b) $\frac{7}{25}$.	(b)	0.28
11	Find the distance covered in 20 min at an average speed of 15 km/h.		5 km
12	8% of a sum of money is 24p. Find the whole amount.		£ 3·00

C

			ANSWER
1	Write each of the following to the nearest whole unit. (a) 8.502 kg	(a)	9 kg
	(b) 6.920 ℓ	(b)	7 ℓ
2	How many pots of jam costing 80p each can be bought for £4·80?		6
3		2.5 0.025 0.25 25.0	
	Which of these decimals is equal to (a) 25% (b) $2\frac{1}{2}$% ?	(a) 0.25 (b)	0.025
4	When loaded a truck has a mass of 6.750 t. The mass of the empty truck is 2050 kg. What is the mass of the load in tonnes?		4.7 t
5	The area of the circle is 321 cm². Find the area of the shaded sector. (240°)		107 cm²
6	A park is approximately 300 m square. What is its approximate area in ha?		9 ha
7	A discount of £8 was allowed when paying a bill of £64. Write the discount as (a) a vulgar fraction in its lowest terms	(a)	$\frac{1}{8}$
	(b) a percentage.	(b)	$12\frac{1}{2}$%
8	The mass of £1s worth of 1p coins is 356 g. What is the mass of 25 of the coins?		89 g
9	The line AB has been drawn to the scale 1 cm to 5 km. Find the distance represented by the line.		27 km
10	Estimate the bearing of (a) point Y from V	(a)	135°
	(b) point V from X.	(b)	045°
11	The population of a town in 1950 was 1.0 million. By the year 2000 there will be a 10% increase. Write in millions the population in the year 2000.		1.1 million
12	This is the net of a box. When the box is made, what will be (a) the surface area	(a)	250 cm²
	(b) the volume?	(b)	250 cm³

Next work Progress Test 2 on page 30.

Enter the result and the date on the chart.

PROGRESS TEST 2

Write the numbers 1 to 20 down the side of a sheet of paper.
Write alongside these numbers the **answers only** to the following questions.
Work as quickly as you can.
Time allowed – **10 minutes.**

1 $\dfrac{3.720}{8} =$ 0.465

2  By how many cm is the perimeter of the rhombus greater than the perimeter of the rectangle?   2 cm

3   Add 145 000 to 1.7 million. Answer in figures.   1 845 000

4   How many 125-mm lengths can be cut from 2.5 m?   20

5 $68.7 = 100\,y$ Find the value of y.   0.687

6   How many days inclusive from 20th April to 2nd June?   44 days

7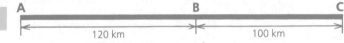

A motorist travels from A to B in $1\frac{1}{2}$ h. If he travels at the same average speed, how long will it take him to travel from B to C? $1\frac{1}{4}$ h (1 h 15 min)

8   Write the larger amount when £144 is divided in the ratio 3:5.   £90

9    Find in degrees the measurement of ∠ x.   90°

10   In a sale, a table costing £625 was reduced by 20%. Find the sale price.   £500

11   Mrs Ferguson received £674·20 for four weeks' work. Find to the nearest £ the average weekly wage.   £169

12   10 articles cost £5·65. Find the cost of 8.   £4·52

13   3 eggs of a box of 150 eggs were broken. What percentage of the eggs were broken?   2%

14   The net mass of a tin of beans is 439 g. Find to the nearest kg the total net mass of 20 tins.   9 kg

15 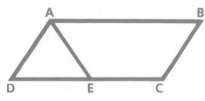 The figure ABCD is a parallelogram.
The triangle AED is an equilateral triangle.
By how many degrees is ∠ C greater than ∠ B?   60°

16   A map is drawn to a scale of 1:250. What distance in m does a line 100 mm long represent?   25 m

17   7 kg of sugar are used in 6 weeks. Write in kg correct to the first decimal place the average amount used each week.   1.2 kg

18   Find the cost of 2 kg 100 g at 45p per $\frac{1}{2}$ kg.   £1·89

19   The marks scored in two tests were $\frac{40}{50}$ and $\frac{18}{20}$. Find as a percentage the average score.   85%

20 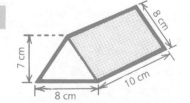 Find the surface area in cm² of the triangular prism.   296 cm²

PROGRESS TEST 2

You will work Progress Test 2 at **four** different times. When you first work the test
    (a) colour the first column to show the number of examples correct out of 20
    (b) enter the date.
Each time you work the test, enter the result and the date in the marked columns.

number of examples correct	1st	2nd	3rd	4th
20				
19				
18				
17				
16				
15				
14				
13				
12				
11				
10				
9				
8				
7				
6				
5				
4				
3				
2				
1				
0				
date				

31

A

		ANSWER
1	435 g + 370 g + 265 g = ▢ kg	1.070 kg
2	7% of 6 m = ▢ cm	42 cm
3	5.3 − 0.19	5.11
4	$4x = 19$ Find the value of x.	4.75 ($4\frac{3}{4}$)
5	Write in figures 0.65 million.	650 000
6	1.55 × 8	12.40
7	1.3 km − 750 m = ▢ m	550 m
8	£4·57 × 6	£ 27·42
9	376 min = ▢ h ▢ min	6 h 16 min
10	$10^3 − 10^2$	900
11	Write as a decimal $5 + \frac{23}{1000}$.	5.023
12	£3·60 ÷ 20 = ▢ p	18p

B

		ANSWER
1	Find in m the total of 6 m, 90 cm, 7 cm and 8 mm.	6.978 m
2	Increase £50 by 4%.	£ 52
3	What is the area of the largest triangle that can be cut from a square of 8-cm side?	32 cm²
4	How many days inclusive from 2nd July to 5th September?	66 days
5	Find the change from £5 after spending 36p and £1·58.	£ 3·06
6	Write to the nearest 1p (a) £0·345	(a) 35p
	(b) £1·014.	(b) £ 1·01
7	Write these numbers putting in a decimal point so that the value of the 3 in each is equal to 3 hundredths. (a) 463	(a) 4.63
	(b) 536	(b) 0.536
	(c) 1003	(c) 10.03
8	Write $\frac{1}{3}$ as a decimal fraction correct to two decimal places.	0.33
9	How many g in 65% of 1 kg?	650 g
10	20 articles cost £6·60. Find the cost of 8.	£ 2·64
11	Find the total in litres of (650 mℓ × 4) and 0.4 ℓ.	3.0 ℓ
12	A car travels 30 km in 36 min. Find its speed in km/h.	50 km/h

C

		ANSWER
1	Subtract £1·60 from the total of 12 TWENTIES, 5 TENS and 7 FIVES.	£ 1·65
2	A pen was bought for £2 and sold at a profit of 45%. Find the selling price.	£ 2·90
3	15 12 18 51 21 Which digit other than 1 is a factor of all these numbers?	3
4	175 rem. 5 6 ⟌ x What number does x represent?	1055
5	£2·40 1·36 0·39 Indira received 35p in change after paying this bill with FIFTIES. How many FIFTIES did she give to pay the bill?	9 FIFTIES
6	The gross mass of a tank of water is 7.250 kg. There are 4.750 ℓ in the tank. What is the mass of the tank in kg?	2.5 kg
7	Find in mm² the area of (a) the parallelogram	(a) 600 mm²
	(b) the shaded triangle.	(b) 300 mm²
8	Daniel has £20 to spend in 7 days. How much is this per day to the nearest 10p?	£ 2·90
9	(a) Name the angle which is vertically opposite to ∠ CYA.	(a) ∠ BYD
	(b) Write its measurement in degrees.	(b) 60°
	(c) Write the measurement in degrees of ∠ CYB.	(c) 120°
10	OFFICE OPENS 8.50 a.m. CLOSES FOR LUNCH 12.15 p.m. to 1.45 p.m. OFFICE CLOSES 5.15 p.m. For how many h and min is the office open each day?	6 h 55 min
11	Meals for 8 people cost £120·00. How much will 10 meals cost at the same rate?	£ 150
12	A 4-cm line on a plan represents a distance of 10 m. (a) What does 1 cm represent?	(a) 2.5 m (250 cm)
	(b) Write the scale as a fraction and as a ratio.	(b) $\frac{1}{250}$ 1:250

Section 3   Test 2

A

		ANSWER
1	$\frac{2}{3} \times 120$	80
2	$(156 + 64) -$ ▨ $= 123$	97
3	3.014×100	301.4
4	$\frac{£48}{5} = £$ ▨	£ 9·60
5	6.5% of £8·00	52p
6	860 m + 312 m + 140 m = ▨ km	1.312 km
7	Find the cost of 2.5 m at £1·40 per m.	£ 3·50
8	5 FIFTIES + 3 TWENTIES + ▨ FIVES = £3·35	5 FIVES
9	350 kg × 6 = ▨ tonnes	2.1 t
10	2 min 43 s + 5 min 38 s	8 min 21 s
11	$x + 1.15 = 2.2$ Find the value of x.	1.05
12	£2·50 × 36	£ 90·00

B

		ANSWER
1	How many pence remain when £24·13 is divided by 10?	3p
2	Write 3.454 kg to the nearest 100 g.	3.5 kg
3	The average of 8 numbers is 25. Find the sum of the numbers.	200
4	What percentage is (a) 15p of £3	(a) 5%
	(b) 40p of £2?	(b) 20%
5	How many times greater is 30.7 than 3.07?	10
6	Write $\frac{25}{30}$ in its lowest terms.	$\frac{5}{6}$
7	One article costs 11p. Find the cost of (a) 100	(a) £ 11·00
	(b) 500.	(b) £ 55·00
8	How many cm more than 2 m is the perimeter of a regular hexagon of side 35 cm?	10 cm
9	1000 × 100 × 10. Write the answer in words.	one million
10	Find in tonnes the total mass of 50 crates each having a mass of 40 kg.	2 t
11	How many pieces of tape each 12.5 cm long can be cut from 2 m of tape?	16
12	A square has an area of 0.16 m². Find (a) the length of one side in m	(a) 0.4 m
	(b) the perimeter in cm.	(b) 160 cm

C

		ANSWER
1	A loaded truck has a mass of 4.180 t. The mass of the truck when empty is 3.200 t. Find, in kg, the mass of the goods carried.	980 kg
2	Write the distance between X and Y (a) in mm	(a) 48 mm
	(b) in cm	(b) 4.8 cm
	(c) in m.	(c) 0.048 m
3	How many $\frac{1}{4}$-litre glasses can be filled from a $3\frac{1}{2}$-litre cask?	14
4	An aircraft travels at a speed of 1800 km/h. How far will it travel in (a) 1 minute	(a) 30 km
	(b) 1 second?	(b) 500 m
5	A pile of 1p coins is 3 cm high. Each coin is 1.5 mm thick. What is the total value of the coins?	20p
6	What volume of concrete in m³ is needed to cover the base to a depth of 10 cm?	1 m³
7	Mandeep sold his cycle for £45 which was 50% less than its cost price. How much did the cycle cost at first?	£ 90
8	Emily's watch loses 2 minutes each day. How many seconds is this per hour?	5 s
9	Find the cost per sheet to the nearest penny when buying	STATIONERY 100 sheets £2·55 1000 sheets £20·20
	(a) 100 sheets	(a) 3p
	(b) 1000 sheets.	(b) 2p
10	Wooden strips 10 cm wide are used to cover a floor 4 m long and 3.5 m wide. Find the total length of the strips.	140 m
11	A model aeroplane is made to a scale of 1:50. If the span of the wings of the model is 30 cm, what is the actual length in m of the span of the aircraft's wings?	15 m
12	By how many m is the distance from A to C via B less than the distance from C to B via A?	700 m

Section 3 Test 3

A

		ANSWER
1	32 + 29 + 58 + 70	189
2	$9^2 - 1^2$	80
3	£1·67 × 9	£ 15·03
4	$\frac{£6·88}{8} = \quad$ p	86p
5	(0.1 + 0.15) × 4	1.0
6	37 hours ÷ 5 = ⬚ h ⬚ min	7 h 24 min
7	$(7 \times 10^5) + (4 \times 10^4) +$ (8×10^3)	748 000
8	$\frac{5}{8}$ of 2400	1500
9	2 km × 0.25 = ⬚ m	500 m
10	99% of 1 kg = ⬚ g	990 g
11	50 mm × 20 = ⬚ m	1 m
12	£5 − (£1·37 + £2·45)	£ 1·18

B

		ANSWER
1	Write the number which is half-way between 1.5 and 2.0.	1·75
2	Reduce £30 by 6%.	£ 28·20
3	Write $8\frac{5}{9}$ as an improper fraction.	$\frac{77}{9}$
4	What percentage of a sum of money remains after 12.5% has been spent?	87.5 %
5	How many tens are there in one hundred thousand?	10 000
6	1,0,8,6,5 Arrange these digits to make the largest possible even number.	86 510
7	Approximate (a) £16·28 to the nearest 10p	(a) £ 16·30
	(b) 14.75 to one decimal place.	(b) 14.8
8	Find in m the perimeter of a regular pentagon of side 840 mm.	4.200 m
9	Write $\frac{2}{3}$ as a decimal correct to two decimal places.	0.67
10	How many pence have the same value as £1000?	100 000 p
11	(a) How many times can 20 be subtracted from 495?	(a) 24
	(b) What is the remainder?	(b) 15
12	The base of a triangle is 1 m and its height is 50 cm. Find its area in cm².	2500 cm²

C

		ANSWER
1	Find in cm³ the volume of the solid.	1800 cm³
2	How many articles costing 8p each can be bought for £30?	375
3	The lines AB and CD are parallel. ∠ w is 60°. Find (a) alternate angle x	(a) 60°
	(b) corresponding angles y and z.	(b) each 120°
4	Find the interest on £150 for one year at $8\frac{1}{2}$%.	£ 12·75
5	Find in degrees the bearing of R from P.	045°
6	Find to the nearest penny the cost of one when (a) 10 cost 73p	(a) 7p
	(b) 10 cost £1·15.	(b) 12p
7	Lucy walks 188 m and then 162 m twice daily. How many km does she walk in 20 days?	14 km
8	Find the area of (a) the triangle	(a) 75 cm²
	(b) the shaded shape.	(b) 725 cm²
9	The cooking time for a chicken is given as 20 min per 400 g plus a further 20 min. (a) Find the time required for a 2 kg chicken.	(a) 2 h
	(b) The meal is to be at 1.15 p.m. At what time must cooking commence?	(b) 11.15 a.m.
10	A 5-litre can of Washo costs £1·00. If 250 mℓ are used each day, what is the cost per day?	5p
11	A set of science books costs £15. How long does is take to pay for them at 75p per week?	20 weeks
12	The graph shows the time taken by a girl to walk 1 km. (a) How many min does it take to walk 1 km?	(a) 9 min
	(b) Estimate to the nearest 100 m the distance walked in 5 min.	(b) 600 m

34

Section 3 Test 4

A

		ANSWER
1	$(37p + 28p) - (13p + 42p)$	10p
2	$7 \times £y = £10\cdot36$ Find the value of y.	£ 1·48
3	$3.5 - \boxed{} = 0.05$	3.45
4	$2\frac{1}{8} + 1\frac{1}{4} + 1\frac{3}{8}$	$4\frac{3}{4}$
5	$3\frac{1}{2}$ years $= \boxed{}$ months	42 months
6	10% of 1.5 $\ell = \boxed{}$ mℓ	150 mℓ
7	7 FIFTIES + 15 FIVES = £ $\boxed{}$	£ 4·25
8	$£24\cdot00 \div 100 = \boxed{}$ p	24p
9	800 kg $\times \boxed{} = 5.6$ t	7
10	45 cm $-$ (55 mm $\times$ 6) $= \boxed{}$ cm	12 cm
11	$\frac{847}{90} = \boxed{}$ rem. $\boxed{}$	9 rem. 37
12	$£1\cdot25 \times 24$	£ 30

B

		ANSWER
1	Find the number which is 95% greater than 100.	195
2	How many sixths remain when $\frac{1}{3}$ is subtracted from $\frac{1}{2}$?	$\frac{1}{6}$
3	$\begin{array}{l} xy \\ 8.379 \end{array}$ Write as a decimal the difference in value between the figure marked x and the figure marked y.	0.061
4	From the sum of £28·50 and £13·75 deduct £10·25.	£ 32·00
5	$\boxed{0.6 \times 4 = 2.4}$ Now find (a) 0.6×0.4 (a) (b) 0.6×0.04. (b)	(a) 0.24 (b) 0.024
6	The area of a triangle is 36 cm². Its height is 6 cm. Find the length of the base.	12
7	Find the total length in m of 144 strips each 0.25 m long.	36 m
8	6 articles cost £15. Find the cost of (a) 2 (b) 5.	(a) £ 5·00 (b) £ 12·50
9	Find the product of 18, 5 and 4.	360
10	Write 750 mℓ of 3 ℓ as (a) a fraction in its lowest terms (b) a percentage.	$\frac{1}{4}$ 25%
11	Multiply 1 h 25 min by 5.	7 h 5 min
12	Increase £1·76 by 10%. Give the answer to the nearest penny.	£ 1·94

C

		ANSWER
1	How many square tiles of side 20 cm are needed to cover the floor?	300
2	When it is noon in London it is 07.00 on the same day in New York. What is the time in New York when it is 14.40 in London?	09.40
3	Find in degrees the size of $\angle$ a, $\angle$ b and $\angle$ c.	$\angle$ a 51° $\angle$ b 76° $\angle$ c 104°
4	A sum of money was divided between Riaz and Ali in the ratio of 3:2. Riaz received the larger share. Write the amount each received (a) as a fraction (b) as a percentage.	

	Riaz	Ali
(a)	$\frac{3}{5}$	$\frac{2}{5}$
(b)	60%	40%

		ANSWER
5	Three 5-mℓ spoonfuls of medicine are to be taken daily for two weeks. How many mℓ are required?	210 mℓ
6	25 articles cost £2·40. (a) Find the cost of 100. (b) Find to the nearest penny the cost of 1.	(a) £ 9·60 (b) 10p
7	What is the highest common factor of 16, 32 and 56?	8
8	Multiply 15p by (a) 5 (b) 50 (c) 500.	(a) 75p (b) £ 7·50 (c) £ 75·00
9	The mass of the box when empty is 375 g. Find the total gross mass of four full boxes. net mass 1.125 kg	6 kg
10	A map is drawn to a scale of 1 mm to 1 m. What length of line in mm represents a distance of 0.3 km?	300 mm
11	Father increased Amy's savings by 10% when he gave her £2·50. How much had she saved?	£ 25·00
12		

BRAND X £2·80 for 3.5 kg	BRAND Z £1·26 for 1.5 kg

Which is the better buy, brand X or brand Z and by how much per kg?

brand X by 4p

Turn back to page 30 and work for the second time Progress Test 2. Enter the result and the date on the chart.

35

A

		ANSWER
1	£0·175 × 2 = ▨ p	35p
2	5.5% of £4 = ▨ p	22p
3	4.056 kg + ▨ g = 4.750 kg	694 g
4	(9 × 10⁶) + (3 × 10⁵) + (6 × 10³)	9 306 000
5	£50·04 ÷ 3	£ 16·68
6	($\frac{7}{8}$ of 56) + ($\frac{2}{3}$ of 30)	69
7	£0·34 × 50 = £ ▨	£ 17·00
8	$\frac{17}{25} = \frac{▨}{100} = ▨$ %	$\frac{68}{100}$ = 68%
9	3 m ÷ 6 = ▨ mm	500 mm
10	250 mℓ × 16 = ▨ ℓ	4 ℓ
11	$9\overline{)\begin{smallmatrix}4.194\\x\end{smallmatrix}}$ Find the value of x.	37.746
12	500 − (5 × 8 × 7)	220

B

		ANSWER
1	By how many is 100 000 less than 1 million? Write the answer in figures.	900 000
2	Find the product of 30 and $3\frac{2}{5}$.	102
3	Find the difference between 1 min 43.5 s and 1 min 47.4 s.	3.9 s
4	How many 0.3-m lengths can be cut from 7.5 m?	25
5	By how many hundredths is $\frac{3}{4}$ more than 0.7?	5 hundredths
6	Share £35 in the ratio 5:2.	£ 25 £ 10
7	The area of a parallelogram is 12.64 m². The base is 8 m long. Find the height in m.	1.58 m
8	Multiply £40 by 19.	£ 760
9	What percentage of 4 m is 50 cm?	$12\frac{1}{2}$ %
10	Find the total contents in litres of 8 bottles each containing 355 mℓ.	2.840 ℓ
11	$\frac{3}{4}$ of a sum of money is £1·50. Find the whole amount.	£ 2·00
12	0.8 ÷ 4 = 0.2 Now find 0.8 ÷ 0.4.	2.0

C

		ANSWER
1	One litre costs £4·20. Find the cost of 1.750 ℓ.	£ 7·35
2	(time line graphic) 2000 BC ... Birth of Christ	
	(a) How many centuries does the time line represent?	(a) 40
	(b) How many years are represented on the time line from X to Y?	(b) 1800
3	At a garden fête, 100 TENS were placed edge to edge in a straight line. The diameter of a TEN is 24.5 mm. Find the length of the line in m.	2.45 m
4	Write 30 cm of 1 metre as (a) a fraction in its lowest terms	(a) $\frac{3}{10}$
	(b) a ratio	(b) 3:10
	(c) a percentage.	(c) 30%
5	The volume of a cube is 1000 cm³. Find (a) the length of one edge	(a) 10 cm
	(b) the total surface area in cm².	(b) 600 cm²
6	James bought foreign stamps for 4p each and then sold them for 10p each. Find his profit per cent on the cost price.	150%
7	The shape is a regular hexagon. (a) How many degrees are there in each angle at the centre?	(a) 60°
	(b) How many degrees are there in each angle at the centre of a regular octagon?	(b) 45°
8	'Round off' each quantity to the nearest whole unit and then find the approximate answer. (a) 9.018 ℓ × 24	(a) 216 ℓ
	(b) 6.72 m × 18	(b) 126 m
9	(diagram: Tinley — 7.25 km — 1.75 km — Sten — 4.5 km — Coty) Walking at a speed of 6 km/h, how long will it take to walk from (a) Sten to Coty	(a) $\frac{3}{4}$ h (45 min)
	(b) Tinley to Coty?	(b) $2\frac{1}{4}$ h (2 h 15 min)
10	C = 2πr π = 3.14 Find the circumference of a circle with radius 10 cm.	62.8 cm
11	The area of a rectangular field is 2.5 ha. The width is 100 m. Find the length.	250 m
12	JAMES 11 years 6 months / TOM 12 years 4 months / LEAH 10 years 2 months Find the average age of the children.	11 years 4 months

Section 3 Test 6

A

		ANSWER
1	24 + 17 + 46	87
2	725 g × 8 = ▨ kg	5.8 kg
3	77p × 7 = £ ▨	£ 5·39
4	$\frac{3x}{2} = 6$ Find the value of x.	4
5	5% of 1.200 kg = ▨ g	60 g
6	0.054 m = ▨ cm	5.4 cm
7	£10·00 − (£3·79 + £2·81)	£ 3·40
8	75 mℓ × 1000 = ▨ ℓ	75 ℓ
9	8 × £y = £10·16 Find the value in £s of y.	£ 1·27
10	0.01 × 0.1	0.001
11	2.88 9) ▨.▨▨	25.92
12	4 tonnes cost £10. Find the cost of 3 t.	£ 7·50

B

		ANSWER
1	Write as a percentage 8·5p in the £.	8.5 %
2	How many times greater is 6.0 than 0.5?	12
3	Add sixty thousand to a quarter of a million.	310 000
4	Which of the following are prime numbers? 17, 27, 37, 47, 57	17 37 47
5	Increase £2·50 by $\frac{2}{5}$.	£ 3·50
6	How many cm² are left after cutting away a 2-cm square from a square of 100 cm²?	96 cm²
7	Find the ratio of (a) 60p to £1·80	(a) 1:3
	(b) 1 mm to 4.5 m.	(b) 1:4500
8	One article costs 12p. Find the cost of 200.	£ 24·00
9	How many 750-mℓ bottles can be filled from 3 litres?	4
10	Write 875 g of 1 kg as (a) a decimal fraction	(a) 0.875
	(b) a fraction in its lowest terms.	(b) $\frac{7}{8}$
11	Express 50 ÷ 9 (a) as a mixed number	(a) $5\frac{5}{9}$
	(b) as a decimal correct to two places.	(b) 5.56
12	How much greater is the total of £2·45 and £3·55 than £18 divided by 4?	£ 1·50

C

		ANSWER
1	475 mm 43 cm 0.575 m 0.6 m Which of the measurements is nearest to $\frac{1}{2}$ m?	475 mm
2	Mr Brown missed the 08.44 train by 7 min. How long did he have to wait for the next train at 10.17?	1 h 26 min
3	By how many metres is 820 m less than 1.250 km?	430 m
4	The lines AB and CD are parallel. Find in degrees ∠ x	126°
	and ∠ y.	54°
5	The estimated population of Mexico City is 18 750 000. Write the population (a) in millions as a decimal	(a) 18.75 millions
	(b) to the nearest 100 000.	(b) 18 800 000
6	56 × 27 = 1512 Find (a) 28 × 27	(a) 756
	(b) 27)15.12.	(b) 0.56
7	π is approximately $3\frac{1}{7}$. Write $3\frac{1}{7}$ as (a) an improper fraction	(a) $\frac{22}{7}$
	(b) a decimal correct to two places.	(b) 3.14
8	20 tins of fruit were bought for £10·60 and sold for £12·40. What was the profit on each tin?	9p
9	One adult fare and 3 half-price fares cost £10. Find the cost of one adult fare.	£ 4·00
10	Find the perimeter of the shaded semicircle. (C = πd π = 3.14) 100 mm	257 mm
11	The scale of a plan is 1:250. What is the actual length in metres represented by a line on the plan which measures 40 mm?	10 m

4.

54° B
A $x°$ D
C $y°$

10.

12.

SCHOOL	Barsby	Clinton	St. Peter's
Number of children	100	200	300
Number of passes	92	165	270

These are the results of a cycling proficiency test. Write each school's number of passes as a percentage of the number of children.

Barsby	92 %
Clinton	82.5 %
St. Peter's	90 %

Section 3　Test 7

A

		ANSWER
1	$(8 \times 7 \times 0) + (8 + 7 + 0)$	15
2	▨ $\times \frac{1}{2} = 6$	12
3	Find the cost of 125 g at £1·24 per $\frac{1}{2}$ kg.	31p
4	£7·04 ÷ 8	88 p
5	0.7 million + 0.5 million Answer in figures.	1 200 000
6	£4·05 × 10	£　40·50
7	3650 mm + ▨ mm = 5 m	1350 mm
8	30% of £5	£　1·50
9	$\frac{£2·40}{6} + 60p = £$ ▨	£　1·00
10	(480 m + 530 m) × 2 = ▨ km	2.020 km
11	$\frac{x}{10} = 2.76$　Find the value of x.	27.6
12	(600 mℓ × 5) ÷ 2 = ▨ ℓ	1.5 ℓ

B

		ANSWER
1	How much less than 50 is $\frac{2}{7}$ of 28?	42
2	Add twenty to thirty-nine thousand nine hundred and eighty. Answer in figures.	40 000
3	Find the whole amount when 30% is 75p.	£　2·50
4	Using index notation write $3 \times 3 \times 3 \times 3 \times 3 \times 3$.	3^6
5	1000 pencils cost £95. Find the cost of (a) 10	(a)　95p
	(b) 40.	(b) £　3·80
6	Find the difference in mℓ between 0.75 of 800 mℓ and 0.7 of 1ℓ.	100 mℓ
7	Write as a decimal (a) $\frac{1}{50}$	(a)　0.02
	(b) $\frac{1}{25}$.	(b)　0.04
8	A length of 3.75 m is cut into 6 equal parts. Find the length in mm of each part.	625 mm
9	Find the ratio of (a) 800 mℓ to 4 ℓ	(a)　1:5
	(b) 6 kg to 600 g.	(b)　10:1
10	Write $\frac{1}{6}$ correct to two decimal places.	0.17
11	Subtract the sum of 780 mm and 52 cm from 2 m.	700 mm
12	The area of a rectangle is 450 cm². The length is 30 cm. Find the width in cm.	15 cm

C

		ANSWER
1	100 TWOS weigh 0.712 kg. Find the mass in g of £1s worth of TWOS.	356 g
2	20　　17　　0　　11　　These scores were made with 4 darts. Find the average score.	12
3	TELEVISION SET £200　　$8\frac{1}{2}$ % interest per annum　　If the set is paid for in 6 months what will be the cost?	£　208·50
4	Daniel and Katie shared their money in the ratio of 4:3. Daniel's share was £12 which was the larger amount. How much was Katie's share?	£　9
5	A bottle of tonic water holds 450 mℓ. Find in ℓ the contents of 50 bottles.	22.5 ℓ
6	∠ a is twice the size of ∠ b. ∠ c is three times the size of ∠ b. Find in degrees ∠ a, ∠ b and ∠ c. ∠ a　120 °	
		∠ b　60 °
		∠ c　180 °
7	Ali was born on 1st Oct. '04. How old will he be in years and months on 1st Feb. 2020?	15 years　4 months
8	Find the cost to the nearest penny of one article when 50 articles cost £3·80.	8p
9	How many lines of symmetry has (a) a regular pentagon	(a)　5
	(b) a regular octagon?	(b)　8
10	3 m of cloth is divided into 9 equal pieces. Write to the nearest cm the length of one piece.	33 cm
11	£2·75　1·63　4·25　Find the change from a £10 note after paying this bill.	£　1·37
12	Area of a circle = πr² π = 3.14　Find the mm² the area of a circle of radius 10 mm.	314 mm²

Section 3 Test 8

A

		ANSWER
1	2 tonnes − 850 kg = ▮ tonnes	1.150 t
2	'Round off' 4 546 000 to the nearest hundred thousand.	'4 500 000
3	$\frac{1}{2} +$ ▮ $= \frac{11}{12}$	$\frac{5}{12}$
4	68p + 27p + £1·16 = £ ▮	£ 2·11
5	275 mm × 6 = ▮ m	1.650 m
6	44p × 9 = £ ▮	£ 3·96
7	1 kg costs 70p. Find the cost of 600 g.	42p
8	12 × 5 × 20	1200
9	$33\frac{1}{3}$ % of £51	£ 17·00
10	£13·00 − £ ▮ = £8·36	£ 4·64
11	5.0 × 0.5	2.5
12	$\frac{£4·02}{7} =$ ▮ p rem. ▮ p.	57p rem. 3p

B

		ANSWER
1	How many hundredths more than $\frac{1}{4}$ is 0.31?	6 hundredths
2	How many ℓ and mℓ in $\frac{3}{8}$ of 10 litres?	3 ℓ 750 mℓ
3	The square root of 100 is 10. Find the square root of 10 000.	100
4	40 articles cost £22. Find the cost of 8 articles.	£ 4·40
5	Find the sum of the prime numbers between 60 and 70.	128
6	How much is 150% of £3·50?	£ 5·25
7	How many times is 125 mℓ contained in (a) 0.5 ℓ	(a) 4
	(b) 2.75 ℓ ?	(b) 22
8	4583 − 2694 —— 1889	Use the example to find (a) 2694 + 1889 (b) 4583 − 1889.	(a) 4583 (b) 2694
9	The perimeter of a rectangle is 54 cm. The breadth is half that of the length. Find (a) the length	(a) 18 cm
	(b) the breadth.	(b) 9 cm
10	What number when multiplied by 6 has a product of 39.6?	6.6
11	Find in hectares the area of a rectangle 340 m long and 100 m wide.	3.4 ha
12	How many cm less than 8 m is the total of twenty 36-cm lengths?	80 cm

C

		ANSWER
1	23.57 / 23.58 / 23.59 / a / b	The drawings show consecutive readings at minute intervals on a digital clock. Write the next two readings on the clock.	(a) 00.00 (b) 00.01
2	The mass of three-quarters of a cake is $4\frac{1}{2}$ kg. What is the mass of half of the cake?	3 kg
3	A room is 5 m long and 4 m wide. It has a volume of 50 m³. How high is the room?	2.5
4	An aircraft flew from point X on a bearing of 135°. On what bearing must the aircraft be flown to return direct to point X?	315°
5	After saving a regular amount each month for one year Sita had a total of £18. How much had she saved after (a) 3 months	(a) £ 4·50
	(b) 10 months?	(b) £ 15·00
6	James was absent from school 20 times out of a possible attendance of 400. Write as a percentage the number of times he was (a) absent	(a) 5 %
	(b) present.	(b) 95 %
7	BROUGHTON depart 15.38 / CARNLEY arrive 16.28	The distance from Broughton to Carnley is 80 km. Find the average speed of the train in km/h.	96 km/h
8	The attendances at four football matches were 29 758, 25 495, 24 086, 19 810. 'Round off' each number to the nearest thousand and find the approximate total attendance.	99 000
9	5 melons of equal value cost £5·40. Find the value of 3 of the melons.	£ 3·24
10	What is the distance from Ash to Rost (a) in m (b) in km?	(a) 2400 m (b) 2.4 km
11	C = πd / π = 3.14	By how many cm is the circumference of the circle less than the perimeter of the square?	4.3 cm
12	1 cm on a map represents an actual distance of 600 m. Write the scale of the map as a ratio.	1:60 000

Turn back to page 30 and work for the third time Progress Test 2. Enter the result and the date on the chart.

Section 3 Test 9

A | ANSWER

1	$2300 + 970 + 1700$	4970
2	$490 ÷ \square = 6$ rem. 10	80
3	27% of 1 tonne = $\square$ kg	270 kg
4	$(15 × 8) ÷ 6$	20
5	$379 m + 221 m = \square$ km	0.6 km
6	$\frac{£2·50 × 6}{3} = £\square$	£ 5·00
7	(a) $\frac{1}{2}\ell + x$ ml $= 615$ ml Find x.	(a) 115 ml
	(b) $\frac{1}{2}\ell - 368$ ml $= y$ ml Find y.	(b) 132 ml
8	(a) $0.3 × 0.2$	(a) 0.06
	(b) $0.06 ÷ 0.2$	(b) 0.3
9	$\frac{1}{4} + \frac{5}{16}$	$\frac{9}{16}$
10	$2.475 m ÷ 9 = \square$ mm	275 mm
11	$4897 ÷ 50 = 97$ rem. $\square$	47
12	$\boxed{248 × 16 = 3968}$	
	$24.8 × 1.6 = \square$	39.68

B | ANSWER

1	How many quarters are there in 36?	144
2	Write as a fraction in its lowest terms (a) $\frac{4}{100}$ (b) $\frac{45}{100}$ (c) $\frac{28}{100}$.	(a) $\frac{1}{25}$ (b) $\frac{9}{20}$ (c) $\frac{7}{25}$
3	1 kg costs £4·00. Find the cost of 700 g.	£ 2·80
4	Find the product of 20 and 0.005.	0.1
5	How many cm remain when 268 cm are taken from 3.4 m?	72 cm
6	Write to the nearest second place of decimals (a) 53.176	(a) 53.18
	(b) 24.694.	(b) 24.69
7	Find the average of 1.1, 2.3 and 0.8.	1.4
8	Share 3 kg in the ratio 1:4.	0.6 kg 2.4 kg
9	Increase £3·27 by 300%.	£ 13·08
10	Find the area in cm² of a square of side 1 m.	10 000 cm²
11	Which two numbers have a sum of 20 and a product of 36?	2 18
12	Deduct (£1·15 × 3) from (£18 ÷ 5).	15p

C | ANSWER

1	The approximate population of a city is 1.2 million. The actual population is 1 207 806. Find the difference.	7806
2	Two parcels together have a mass of 18.5 kg. One of them is 4 kg heavier than the other. Find the mass of each parcel.	7.25 kg 11.25 kg
3	Which of these solids will have a circular face when cut horizontally, and a rectangular face when cut vertically? Sphere Cone Cylinder	cylinder
4	In a class of 30 children 12 were absent. Write the number absent as (a) a fraction in its lowest terms	(a) $\frac{2}{5}$
	(b) a ratio.	(b) 2:5
5	A pen costs 35p. How many can be bought for £7·00?	20
6	VWYZ is a rhombus. WXY is an isosceles triangle. Find (a) ∠ WYZ	(a) 112°
	(b) ∠ VWY	(b) 68°
	(c) ∠ ZVW.	(c) 112°
7	Tom has 95p and Sophie has 73p. How much must Tom give to Sophie so that each has the same amount?	11p
8	If 1st July falls on a Thursday how many Saturdays will there be in that month?	5
9	One child in every four in a school of 200 wears spectacles. (a) What percentage do not wear spectacles?	(a) 75%
	(b) How many wear spectacles?	(b) 50
10	The gross mass of a crate is 24 kg. Find the mass in kg of the empty crate which is $\frac{2}{5}$ of the gross mass.	9.6 kg
11	$\boxed{\text{Area of a circle} = πr² \mid π = 3.14}$ The area of the larger circle is twice that of the smaller circle. Find the area of the larger circle.	6.28 m²
12	The graph shows the speed of a car. Use the graph to find the time taken by the car to travel 40 km.	30 min

A

		ANSWER
1	£1·20 × $3\frac{1}{2}$	£ 4·20
2	$\dfrac{2.64 + 3.36}{2}$	3
3	2.25 ℓ − (250 mℓ × 6) = ▢ mℓ	750 mℓ
4	7 FIFTIES + 6 TWENTIES + 9 FIVES = £ ▢	£ 5·15
5	1200 km − (320 km + 280 km + 335 km)	265 km
6	(a) $\frac{1}{8}$ = ▢ %	(a) 12.5 %
	(b) $\frac{3}{8}$ = ▢ %	(b) 37.5 %
7	9.8 ÷ 4	2.45
8	£5·00 − £ ▢ = £2·82	£ 2·18
9	£6 × $\frac{2}{5}$	£ 2·40
10	9x = 33 + 48　Find the value of x.	9
11	Find the cost of 30 cm at £1·80 per m.	54p
12	$\frac{1}{7}$ of 4 kg 60 g = ▢ g	580 g

B

		ANSWER
1	Add $\frac{3}{4}$ of 28 to $\frac{7}{8}$ of 56.	70
2	When was the next leap year after 1985?	1988
3	Increase £3·00 by 7%.	£ 3·21
4	Write $\frac{2}{7}$ as a decimal fraction correct to two places.	0.29
5	Find the total mass in kg of these amounts of water. 2.7 ℓ　95 mℓ　3.4 ℓ	6.195 kg
6	One envelope costs 17p. Find the cost of　(a) 10	(a) £ 1·70
	(b) 1000.	(b) £ 170
7	A rhombus has an area of 100 cm². Its base is 8 cm. Find its height in mm.	125 mm
8	Approximate 4 635 000 to (a) the nearest million	(a) 5 000 000
	(b) the nearest 100 000	(b) 4 600 000
	(c) the nearest 10 000.	(c) 4 640 000
9	How many kg less than 1 tonne is 4 tonnes divided by 5?	200 kg
10	Find the difference in hundredths between 100 × 0.016 and 100 × 0.017.	10 hundredths
11	Express 43 ÷ 5 as (a) a mixed number	(a) $8\frac{3}{5}$
	(b) a decimal.	(b) 8.6
12	Multiply £1·50 by 52.	£ 78·00

C

		ANSWER
1	A cask holds 20.750 ℓ of water. The mass of the cask when empty is 850 g. Find the mass of the cask when it is full.	21.6 kg
2	A is the centre of the circle. (a) Name the triangle ABC by its sides.	(a) isosceles
	(b) Calculate the angle at B.	(b) 35°
3	Six articles cost £8·37. Find to the nearest penny the cost of one article.	£ 1·40
4	There are 4.545 ℓ of bleach in a plastic container. The bleach lasts for 9 weeks. How many mℓ are used on average per week?	505 mℓ
5	FRUIT Bargain Pack (820 g, 820 g, 820 g) There was 87p change from £3 after buying the 'Bargain Pack'. Find the cost of each tin.	71p
6	Find in kg the mass of (a) 1 'Bargain Pack'	(a) 2.460 kg
	(b) 8 'Bargain Packs'.	(b) 19.680 kg
7	A map is drawn to a scale of 1 cm to 1 km. How many m are represented on a map by a line 14 mm long?	1400 m
8	Find (a) the area of the triangular end of the prism	(a) 12 cm²
	(b) the volume of the prism.	(b) 96 cm²
9	A square of 100-m side has an area of 1 ha. A square of 1-km side has an area of 1 km². How many ha are there in 1 km²?	100 ha
10	The price of a pair of shoes costing £25 was increased by £1·25. Write the increase as a percentage.	5 %
11	Write the number of shaded squares (a) as a fraction in its lowest terms	(a) $\frac{3}{10}$
	(b) as a decimal.	(b) 0.3
12	Mr Macleod arrived at a guest house on October 29th and left on November 3rd. The charge for the room was £10·50 per night. What was the total cost of the room?	£ 52·50

Section 3 Test 11

A

		ANSWER
1	2.999 + 0.1	3.099
2	1.5 tonnes + 550 kg = ▩ t	2.050 t
3	6.25% of £4·00	25p
4	£3·24 = ▩ × 2p	162
5	86.6 × 200	17 320
6	5.2 ℓ − 480 mℓ = ▩ ℓ	4.720 ℓ
7	5 x = 28.2 Find the value of x.	5.64
8	11 730 ÷ 25 = 469 rem. ▩	469 rem. 5
9	£2·78 + £2·78 + £2·78 + £2·78 + £2·78	£ 13·90
10	$\dfrac{4\,kg \times 3}{▩}$ = 1500 g	8
11	40 cm cost 50p. Find the cost per m.	£ 1·25
12	495 ÷ ▩ = 8 rem. 15	60

B

		ANSWER
1	(a) £1·32 × 4	(a) £ 5·28
	(b) £1·32 × 16	(b) £ 21·12
2	What must be added to $2\frac{5}{8}$ to make $4\frac{1}{2}$?	$1\frac{7}{8}$
3	Find 8.5% of £10.	85p
4	The perimeter of a rectangle is 30 m. The width is 6.5 m. Find the length.	8.5 m
5	Divide £31·50 in the ratio 5:4.	£ 17·50 £ 14 00
6	1000 articles cost £154·00. Find the cost of one article to the nearest penny.	15p
7	How much less than 20 is the product of 1.7 and 9?	4.7
8	How many thousandths in $\frac{1}{4}$ of 0.02?	5 thousandths
9	Find the difference in mm between 0.7 m and 369 mm.	331 mm
10	Write 150 mℓ of 750 mℓ as (a) a fraction in its lowest terms	(a) $\frac{1}{5}$
	(b) a percentage	(b) 20%
	(c) a ratio.	(c) 1:5
11	'Round off' these amounts to the nearest £1 and then find the approximate answer. £16·70 + £12·95 + £9·28	£ 39
12	$C = 2\pi r$ $\pi = 3.14$ The radius of a circle is 100 cm. Find the circumference in m.	6.28 m

C

		ANSWER
1	3.468×6 Write the answer	
	(a) to three decimal places	(a) 20.808
	(b) to two decimal places	(b) 20.81
	(c) to one decimal place.	(c) 20.8
2	The contents of 4 boxes of matches were 51, 46, 49 and 54. Find the average contents.	50
3	This is a plan of a field. Write its area in ha.	3.5 ha
4	A case of 240 eggs was delivered to a school kitchen. 12 of the eggs were broken. What percentage were (a) broken	(a) 5 %
	(b) not broken?	(b) 95 %
5	F = { 1, 2, 3, 6, ▩, ▩, ▩, 78 } F = the set of factors of 78. Find the missing factors.	13 26 39

6

Time in min	a	24	18
Distance km	50	b	24
Speed km/h	75	90	c

Find the missing time, distance or speed.
(a) 40 min
(b) 36 km
(c) 80 km/h

7	A camera costs £85·50. It can be paid for in 9 equal instalments. Find the cost of each payment.	£ 9·50
8	The drawing is of a regular pentagon. Find in degrees the measurement of ∠ a 72° ∠ b 54° ∠ c 72°	
9	1 g = 1000 milligrams (mg) A medicine bottle contains 120 tablets. Each tablet has a mass of 500 mg. (a) Write the mass of each tablet in g.	(a) 0.5 g or $\frac{1}{2}$ g
	(b) Find in g the total mass of the tablets.	(b) 60 g
10	For the shaded shape find (a) the area	(a) 12 cm²
	(b) the perimeter.	(b) 20 cm
11	A wall 3 m high and 4 m wide is to be covered in wallpaper 50 cm wide. What length in m of the paper is required?	24 m
12	X 1.5 ℓ costing 93p Y 750 mℓ costing 48p Which is the better buy per half-litre and by how much?	X by 1p

Section 3   Test 12

A

		ANSWER
1	(268 + 232) − 350	150
2	2 640 000 = ▓ millions	2.64 millions
3	1 FIFTY − (17p + 16p + 9p)	8p
4	3.5 m − 175 cm = ▓ cm	175 cm
5	$\frac{x}{21} = \frac{2}{3}$ Find the value of x.	14
6	Find the cost of 750 mℓ at £4·80 per ℓ.	£ 3·60
7	$\begin{array}{r}16 \text{ rem. } 4\\ 8\overline{)y}\end{array}$ Find the value of y.	132
8	4 × 18 × 50	3600
9	$\frac{3.8}{1.9}$ = ▓	2
10	(12% of £5) + (8% of £5)	£ 1·00
11	$7\frac{1}{4}$ ℓ ÷ ▓ = 725 mℓ	10
12	£0·14 × 15	£ 2·10

B

		ANSWER
1	Find in cm the perimeter of an equilateral triangle of side 96 mm.	28.8 cm
2	Write the 24-hour clock time which is 1 h 24 min after 22.57.	00.21
3	How many times is 800 g contained in 3.2 kg?	4
4	Divide £85 by 6 (a) to the nearest 10p	(a) £ 14·20
	(b) to the nearest penny.	(b) £ 14·17
5	The total of two amounts is £12 and their difference is £3·60. Find the two amounts.	£ 7·80
		£ 4·20
6	Find the difference in thousands between (1 × 10⁵) and (9 × 10⁴).	10 000
7	Write $3\frac{1}{2}$% as a decimal.	0.035
8	Multiply £2·54 by 1.5.	£ 3·81
9	How many (a) ha in 5 km²	(a) 500 ha
	(b) ha in 7.3 km² ?	(b) 730 ha
10	Increase £15 by 4%.	£ 15·60
11	Write the scale 1 cm to 2 km (a) as a fraction	(a) $\frac{1}{200\,000}$
	(b) as a ratio.	(b) 1:200 000
12	The diameter of a circle is 6 m. Find the area in m². (π = 3.14)	28.26 m²

C

		ANSWER
1	The wholesale price of a football is £15·85 and the retail price is £19·50. Find the profit.	£ 3·65
2	A FIFTY coin has a mass of 13.5 g. What is the mass of £10s worth of FIFTIES?	270 g
3	Write the length of a line 100 times the length of the line AB (a) in mm	(a) 5500 mm
	(b) in cm	(b) 550 cm
	(c) in m.	(c) 5.5 m
4	On a plan of a house the lounge measures 44 mm long and 40 mm wide. The scale of the plan is 1 cm to 1 m. Find in m² the area of the lounge.	17.6 m²
5	Which of the dotted lines are lines of symmetry?	BF HD
6	A man ran 800 m in 1 min 52 s. What was his average time per 100 m?	14 s
7	On a 5-day holiday George walked 14.75 km, 13.760 km, 12.290 km, 10.150 km and 9.320 km. 'Round off' each distance to the nearest km and find the approximate average distance walked daily.	12 km
8	π = 3.14. Find (a) the area of the end of the cylinder	(a) 3.14 cm²
	(b) its volume.	(b) 15.7 cm³
9	Mortar can be made of sand and cement in the ratio 4:1. How many kg of sand are mixed with half a 50-kg bag of cement?	100 kg

10	Mon.	Tues.	Wed.	Thurs.	Fri.
	5°C	3°C	0°C	−1°C	−2°C

Find the average daily temperature.   1°C

11	The mass of an empty bottle is 555 g. The bottle holds 0.710 litres of water. Find the gross mass in kg of the bottle when filled.	1.265 kg
12	These are the results of 3 tests. Write each as a percentage. (a) $\frac{18}{25}$	(a) 72 %
	(b) $\frac{30}{40}$	(b) 75 %
	(c) $\frac{10}{30}$	(c) $33\frac{1}{3}$ %

**Turn back to page 30 and work for the fourth time
Progress Test 2. Enter the result and the date on the chart.**

43

A

(a)		(b)	
12 − 7	5	53 ÷ 7	7 rem. 4
9 + 4	13	(6 × 8) + 5	53
3 × 6	18	70 ÷ 8	8 rem. 6
63 ÷ 9	7	(4 × 9) + 7	43
6 + 9	15	52 ÷ 6	8 rem. 4
7 × 8	56	(7 × 0) + 3	3
11 − 7	4	4 ÷ 9	0 rem. 4
24 ÷ 3	8	(8 × 1) + 6	14
5 + 8	13	61 ÷ 7	8 rem. 5
0 ÷ 7	0	(9 × 4) + 5	41
8 × 6	48	77 × 10	770
64 ÷ 8	8	135 ÷ 10	13 rem. 5
9 × 3	27	35 × 20	700
13 − 7	6	204 ÷ 20	10 rem. 4
7 + 8	15	96 × 30	2880
15 − 9	6	156 ÷ 40	3 rem. 36
0 × 8	0	108 × 60	6480
4 + 6	10	302 ÷ 60	5 rem. 2
40 ÷ 8	5	88 × 70	6160
16 − 7	9	463 ÷ 90	5 rem. 13

B   Write these numbers.

Forty thousand and nine	40 009
Eighty-one thousand two hundred and five	81 205
Two hundred and ten thousand four hundred	210 400
Five hundred and six thousand and seventy	506 070
700 000 + 1000 + 90 + 5	701 095
(4 × 10 000) + (8 × 100) + 9	40 809
1 million	1 000 000
$1\frac{3}{4}$ million	1 750 000
2.6 million	2 600 000
(6 × 10³) + (3 × 10²) + (0 × 10)	6300
(9 × 10⁴) + (7 × 10³) + (1 × 10²) + (3 × 10)	97 130

Write the answers to these as decimals.

206 tenths	20.6
1509 thousandths	1.509
Eighteen hundredths	0.18
$17 + \frac{5}{10} + \frac{3}{1000}$	17.503
$10 + \frac{6}{100} + \frac{7}{1000}$	10.067
$\frac{27}{100} + \frac{8}{1000}$	0.278
$60 + \frac{57}{1000}$	60.057

C   Write in figures the number which is:

Forty less than ten thousand	9960
Nought point six two more than ten	10.62
Five hundred less than fifty-five thousand	54 500
Nine thousand more than $\frac{1}{4}$ million	259 000
Two point seven less than two hundred.	197.3

Write in words the value of the figure underlined.

3̲7 908	seven thousand
1 6̲04 326	six hundred thousand
9.08̲4	eight hundredths
20.50̲2	two thousandths

7.9	=	79 tenths	20.6	206 tenths
0.75	=	75 hundredths	3.09	309 hundredths
0.018	=	18 thousandths	10.06	10 060 thousandths
5.9	=	5900 thousandths	0.003	3 thousandths

Write these numbers omitting the noughts which do not alter the value of the number.

17.09	17.09	8.070	8.07
020.60	20.6	30.020	30.02
002730	2730	106.00	106

D

(a)		(b)	
3.46 + 5.04	8.5	30.08 × 10	300.8
5.16 + 3.9	9.06	2.017 × 100	201.7
1.99 + 2.01	4.00	0.063 × 1000	63
0.76 + 0.493	1.253	3 × 7.8	23.4
2.83 + 7.178	10.008	0.09 × 6	0.54
		6.075 × 8	48.6
3.92 − 1.9	2.02	10.3 ÷ 10	1.03
6.1 − 0.7	5.4	3.7 ÷ 100	0.037
10.0 − 9.348	0.652	46 ÷ 1000	0.046
7.2 − 0.09	7.11	18.36 ÷ 6	3.06
8.63 − 3.58	5.05	2.43 ÷ 9	0.27
5.825 − 0.06	5.765	14.091 ÷ 7	2.013

Find the value of x.

(a)		(b)	
x + 19 = 54	35	10 × x = 3.65	0.365
3.2 + x = 10	6.8	x × x = 36	6
52 − x = 18	34	7x = 108.5	15.5
x − 4.05 = 3.6	7.65	$\frac{x}{5} = 12.8$	64
2.3 + x = 20	17.7	$\frac{72}{x} = 9$	8
x = 17.2 − 5.5	11.7		

E   Approximate to the nearest:

hundred thousand		1.37 million	1.4 million
thousand		79 464	79 000
hundred		23 086	23 100
whole number	(a) $16\frac{1}{3}$ 16	(b) 29.52	30
first decimal place		10.38	10.4
		5.94	5.9
second decimal place		0.025	0.03
		13.004	13.00

F   Work these divisions (a) to 2 decimal places then (b) approximate the answer to the nearest first decimal place.

39 ÷ 8	(a)	4.88	(b)	4.9
5.5 ÷ 3	(a)	1.83	(b)	1.8
14.6 ÷ 7	(a)	2.09	(b)	2.1

Work these divisions to 3 decimal places and then write the answer correct to 2 decimal places.

58 ÷ 6	(a)	9.667	(b)	9.67
34.26 ÷ 9	(a)	3.807	(b)	3.81

CHECK-UP TEST   Money, Measures and Approximations

A   Find the total of each row of coins.

50p	20p	10p	5p	2p	1p	TOTAL
	2	3	4	6		£1·02
2	5	9			13	£3·03
	7		5	8		£1·81
		17	8		12	£2·22
1	3	6		10		£1·90
5	4	7	12			£4·60
11					23	£5·73

B   Find (a) the total cost of the articles bought
(b) the change.

MONEY GIVEN	Cost of articles bought	Total cost	CHANGE
1 FIFTY	9p, 8p, 18p	35p	15p
4 TENS	5 @ 7p each	35p	5p
£1	23p, 18p, 40p	81p	19p
£1 and 1 FIFTY	3 @ 34p + 12p	£ 1·14	36p
£2	10 @ 18p each	£ 1·80	20p
£5 note	£2·75, £1·28	£ 4·03	97p

C

£0·39 = ▓ FIVES + 7 TWOS ___5___
£0·85 = 1 FIFTY + ▓ FIVES ___7___
£1·70 = 2 TENS + ▓ FIFTIES ___3___
£2·80 = 8 FIVES + ▓ TWENTIES ___12___
£4·25 = 7 FIFTIES + ▓ FIVES ___15___

How many articles each costing:
2p for 98p ___49___
3p for £1·74 ___58___
5p for £2·05 ___41___
50p for £18·50 ___37___
20p for £25·20 ___126___
5 for 6p for £1·62 ___135___
7 for 10p for £3·30 ? ___231___

D

10 articles cost £1·20
1 costs ___12p___   7 cost ___84p___

100 articles cost £2·30
10 cost ___23p___   30 cost ___69p___

20 articles cost £3·60
5 cost ___90p___   1 costs ___18p___

8 articles cost £1·44
3 cost ___54p___   7 cost £ 1·26

5 articles cost 85p
1 costs ___17p___   9 cost £ 1·53
40 cost £ 6·80   100 cost £ 17·00

E

39p + 57p + 41p   £ 1·37
£1·06 + £3·70 + £0·28   £ 5·04
£1·36 − 87p   49p
£4·00 − £1·68   £ 2·32
£6·03 − £1·89   £ 4·14
19p × 7   £ 1·33
£2·08 × 9   £ 18·72
£5·78 × 6   £ 34·68
£3·04 ÷ 8   38p
£27 ÷ 4   £ 6·75
£43·45 ÷ 5   £ 8·69

F

55 cm	=	0.55 m
309 mm	=	30.9 cm
5040 mm	=	5.040 m
1095 cm	=	10.95 m
300 m	=	0.3 km
2805 m	=	2.805 km
5000 m	=	5 km
90 g	=	0.090 kg
875 g	=	0.875 kg
3500 g	=	3.5 kg
120 ml	=	0.120 l
650 ml	=	650 cm³

G

20.7 cm	=	207 mm
3.45 m	=	345 cm
10.6 m	=	10 600 mm
0.085 km	=	85 m
7.5 km	=	7500 m
4.385 km	=	4385 m
0.065 kg	=	65 g
8.110 kg	=	8110 g
5.4 l	=	5400 ml
0.75 l	=	750 ml
4.5 l	=	4500 cm³
2.008 l	=	2008 cm³

H   Find the cost of:

100 g @ 70p per kg   ___7p___
400 g @ 45p per kg   ___18p___
250 g @ £1·10 per ½ kg   ___55p___
3.5 kg @ 18p per ½ kg   £ 1·26
450 g @ 70p per ½ kg   ___63p___
75 cm @ £3·00 per m   £ 2·25
10 cm @ £2·90 per m   ___29p___
20 cm @ £4·20 per m   ___84p___
1.25 l @ 36p per ½ l   ___90p___
900 ml @ 60p per l   ___54p___
6.5 m² @ £4·50 per m².   £ 29·25

I   Fill in the missing times.

12-hour clock time	24-hour clock time
10.35 p.m.	22.35
4.10 a.m.	04.10
12.05 a.m.	00.05
11.55 p.m.	23.55

J   How many h and min between:

8.45 a.m. and 11.20 a.m.   2 h 35 min
10.25 a.m. and 1.05 p.m.   2 h 40 min
9.38 p.m. and 2.10 a.m.   4 h 32 min
11.50 and 13.15   1 h 5 min
06.19 and 10.20 ?   4 h 1 min

K   How many days inclusive:

from 28th Mar. to 7th April   11
from 13th May to 4th June   23
from 15th July to 3rd Aug.   20
from 24th Sept. to 8th Nov.   46
from 19th Oct. to 10th Dec.?   53

L   Approximate to the nearest:

£1   (a) £12·09 £ 12·00   (b) £3·52 £ 4·00
10p   (a) £2·37 £ 2·40   (b) £10·06 £ 10·10

Write the answer to the nearest penny.
(a) ⅓ of £7·00 £ 2·33   (b) £3·10 ÷ 7   44p
(c) ⅛ of £17·25 £ 2·16   (d) ¼ of £3·95   99p

Approximate to the nearest:

centimetre	0.837 m	84 cm
metre	305.6 cm	3 m
kilogram	9 kg 550 g	10 kg
litre	6.325 l	6 l
½ kilogram	7.750 kg	8 kg
hour	2 h 29 min	2 h
½ hour	4 h 21 min.	4½ h

CHECK-UP TEST Fractions, Ratios, Percentages and Angles

A Change to decimal fractions. When necessary work to the nearest 2nd place.

(a) $\frac{4}{5}$ ___0.8___ (b) $\frac{1}{6}$ ___0.17___ (c) $\frac{2}{3}$ ___0.67___ (d) $\frac{7}{8}$ ___0.88___ (e) $\frac{5}{7}$ ___0.71___

B

				Express as mixed numbers.
$\frac{1}{3} + \frac{1}{2}$ ___$\frac{5}{6}$___	$\frac{1}{2} - \frac{1}{6}$ ___$\frac{1}{3}$___	$\frac{2}{3} \times 12$ ___8___		$\frac{137}{10}$ ___$13\frac{7}{10}$___
$\frac{1}{4} + \frac{1}{6}$ ___$\frac{5}{12}$___	$\frac{3}{4} - \frac{2}{3}$ ___$\frac{1}{12}$___	$10 \times 1\frac{2}{5}$ ___14___		$93 \div 8$ ___$11\frac{5}{8}$___
$\frac{5}{8} + \frac{3}{4}$ ___$1\frac{3}{8}$___	$3 - 1\frac{7}{12}$ ___$1\frac{5}{12}$___	$1\frac{7}{10} \times 20$ ___34___		$124 \div 9$ ___$13\frac{7}{9}$___
$\frac{3}{10} + 1\frac{1}{2}$ ___$1\frac{4}{5}$___	$2\frac{1}{4} - \frac{7}{8}$ ___$1\frac{3}{8}$___	$40 \times \frac{3}{8}$ ___15___		

C Write each fraction as a ratio in its lowest terms.

(a) $\frac{12}{20}$ ___3:5___ (b) $\frac{28}{40}$ ___7:10___ (c) $\frac{45}{100}$ ___9:20___ (d) $\frac{24}{32}$ ___3:4___ (e) $\frac{30}{48}$ ___5:8___

Write each of these scales (a) as a fraction (b) as a ratio.

1 mm to 20 cm (a) ___$\frac{1}{200}$___ (b) 1:200 ; 1 cm to 5 m (a) ___$\frac{1}{500}$___ (b) 1:500 ; 1 cm to 1 km (a) ___$\frac{1}{100\,000}$___ (b) 1:100 000

D Fill in the table. The first example is done for you.

	FRACTION (lowest terms)	PERCENTAGE %	RATIO
40p of 50p	$\frac{4}{5}$	80%	4:5
300 g of 0.5 kg	$\frac{3}{5}$	60%	3:5
700 mℓ of 1 litre	$\frac{7}{10}$	70%	7:10
5p of £1	$\frac{1}{20}$	5%	1:20

	FRACTION (lowest terms)	PERCENTAGE %	RATIO
50 cm of 2 m	$\frac{1}{4}$	25%	1:4
750 g of 1.5 kg	$\frac{1}{2}$	50%	1:2
250 of 400	$\frac{5}{8}$	62.5%	5:8
35p of £5	$\frac{7}{100}$	7%	7:100

E 8 cost £10. What fraction of £10 do
3 cost ___$\frac{3}{8}$___ 7 cost? ___$\frac{7}{8}$___

5 cost £7. What fraction of £7 do
2 cost ___$\frac{2}{5}$___ 8 cost? ___$\frac{8}{5}$___

10 cost £3·50. What fraction of £3·50 do
9 cost ___$\frac{9}{10}$___ 15 cost? ___$\frac{3}{2}$___

Share each quantity in the given ratio.
£30, ratio 3:2 £ __18__ £ __12__
1.750 kg, ratio 4:1 __1.4 kg__ __350 g__
2 m, ratio 5:3 __125 cm__ __75 cm__

F Find the value of:

$\frac{3}{10}$ of £1·60 ___48p___
0.75 of 600 ___450___
60% of $\frac{1}{2}$ kg ___300 g___
0.9 of 2 ℓ ___1.800 ℓ___
50% of 3 m 70 cm __1m 85 cm__
$\frac{3}{100}$ of 1 kg ___30 g___
0.95 of 10 000 ___9500___
17% of £3·00 ___51p___
$\frac{5}{9}$ of 1.800 kg. ___1 kg___

G Find the whole when:

0.25 is £3·50 £ __14__
$\frac{3}{4}$ is 57 cm __76 cm__
10% is 850 g __8.5 kg__
0.6 is 42p __70p__
$\frac{5}{8}$ is 2.5 kg __4 kg__
30% is 1.8 ℓ __6 ℓ__
0.375 is 300 __800__
$\frac{7}{10}$ is 91p £ __1·30__
5% is 200 g. __4 kg__

H

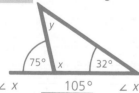

Estimate which of the angles marked $a - h$ is:

a right angle ___b___ an acute angle of 80° ___f___
an obtuse angle of 130° ___a___ a reflex angle of 300° ___e___ a reflex angle of 240°. ___g___

I Find the angle marked x and/or y in each shape.

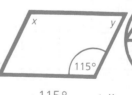

∠ x ___105°___   ∠ x ___35°___   ∠ x ___75°___   ∠ x ___115°___   ∠ x ___90°___   ∠ x ___40°___
∠ y ___43°___   ∠ y ___55°___   ∠ y ___65°___   ∠ y ___40°___

Fill in the table for regular polygons.

NAME of regular polygon	NUMBER OF SIDES	ANGLE AT CENTRE
Hexagon	6	60°
Octagon	8	45°
Pentagon	5	72°

 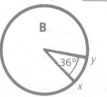

What fraction of the circumference is the arc xy in circle A, circle B? A ___$\frac{1}{3}$___ B ___$\frac{1}{10}$___

CHECK-UP TEST   Shapes, Perimeter, Area and Volume

A   Each of the shapes A to G is a quadrilateral.

A   B   C   D   E   F   G

Give the **letter** of the shape which is: (a) a rhombus __E__   (b) a rectangle __A__
(c) a trapezium __C__   (d) a square __D__   (e) a parallelogram. __G__

Write the **name** of the shape (or shapes) which has:
4 equal sides __square, rhombus__   4 right angles __square, rectangle__
opposite sides equal and parallel __square, rectangle, rhombus, parallelogram__
one pair only of parallel sides __trapezium__
diagonals which are equal __square, rectangle__
diagonals which bisect each other at right angles. __square, rhombus__

Write the **letter** of the shape or shapes which have: (a) no axis of symmetry __B C F G__
(b) 2 axes of symmetry __A E__   (c) 4 axes of symmetry. __D__

B   Fill in the missing measurements. In each case give the unit of measurement.

SQUARES : RECTANGLES	$A = lb$	$b = \dfrac{A}{l}$	$l = \dfrac{A}{b}$
length	**breadth**	**perimeter**	**Area**
7 cm	5.5 cm	25 cm	38.5 cm²
16 cm	6 cm	44 cm	96 cm²
10 cm	8 cm	36 cm	80 cm²
9 cm	3.5 cm	25 cm	31.5 cm²
25 m	20 m	90 m	500 m²

TRIANGLES	$A = \dfrac{bh}{2}$	$b = \dfrac{2A}{h}$	$h = \dfrac{2A}{b}$
base	**height**	**Area**	
35 mm	12 mm	210 mm²	
27 cm	18 cm	243 cm²	
9 cm	6 cm	27 cm²	
11 cm	3 cm	16.5 cm²	
1.6 m	9 m	7.2 m²	

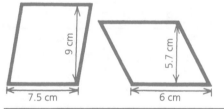

RHOMBUSES AND PARALLELOGRAMS	$A = bh$	$b = \dfrac{A}{h}$	$h = \dfrac{A}{b}$		
base	7.5 cm	6 cm	16 cm	1.5 m	40 cm
height	9.0 cm	5.7 cm	7 cm	3 m	15 mm
Area	67.5 cm²	34.2 cm²	112 cm²	4.5 m²	60 cm²

CIRCLES	$C = \pi d$ or $2\pi r$: $A = \pi r^2$: $\pi = 3.14$		
radius (r)	1 cm	3 cm	10 cm
diameter (d)	2 cm	6 cm	20 cm
circumference (c)	6.28 cm	18.84 cm	62.8 cm
Area (A)	3.14 cm²	28.26 cm²	314 cm²

CUBES, CUBOIDS	$V = lbh$	$l = \dfrac{V}{bh}$	$b = \dfrac{V}{lh}$	$h = \dfrac{V}{bl}$
length	**breadth**	**height**	**Volume**	
8 cm	5 cm	9 cm	360 cm³	
20 cm	20 cm	20 cm	8000 cm³	
8 m	3.5 m	2 m	56 m³	
6.4 cm	10 cm	5 cm	320 cm³	
10 cm	9.3 cm	2 cm	186 cm³	

Find the volume of each of these prisms.

225.0 cm³

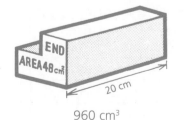

960 cm³

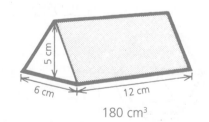

180 cm³

Full list of the *Schofield & Sims Mental Arithmetic* books

Pupil books

Mental Arithmetic Introductory Book	ISBN 978 07217 0798 3
Mental Arithmetic Book 1	ISBN 978 07217 0799 0
Mental Arithmetic Book 2	ISBN 978 07217 0800 3
Mental Arithmetic Book 3	ISBN 978 07217 0801 0
Mental Arithmetic Book 4	ISBN 978 07217 0802 7
Mental Arithmetic Book 5	ISBN 978 07217 0803 4
Mental Arithmetic Book 6	ISBN 978 07217 0804 1

Answers

Mental Arithmetic Introductory Book Answers	ISBN 978 07217 0853 9
Mental Arithmetic Book 1 Answers	ISBN 978 07217 0805 8
Mental Arithmetic Book 2 Answers	ISBN 978 07217 0806 5
Mental Arithmetic Book 3 Answers	ISBN 978 07217 0807 2
Mental Arithwmetic Book 4 Answers	ISBN 978 07217 0808 9
Mental Arithmetic Book 5 Answers	ISBN 978 07217 0809 6
Mental Arithmetic Book 6 Answers	ISBN 978 07217 0810 2

Related materials

For information about the **I can do** teaching method, which you may use with *Schofield and Sims Mental Arithmetic,* watch the film **'I can do maths' in practice** online at **www.schofieldandsims.co.uk/icando/** and order the

I can do maths Teacher's Guide	ISBN 978 07217 1115 7

For A3 Desk Mats with maths facts on one side and English facts on the other – and ample space for writing children's individual targets, order the

I can do Desk Mat (Class set)	Order no. 5060137710000

All available from

Schofield & Sims
Dogley Mill
Fenay Bridge
Huddersfield HD8 0NQ

Web: www.schofieldandsims.co.uk
Tel: 01484 607080
Fax: 01484 606815
E-mail: sales@schofieldandsims.co.uk